D0244284

COOKING
the Weight Watchers Way

WeightWatchers®

COOKING
the Weight Watchers Way

Recipes for the *ProPoints* system with many Filling & Healthy foods

SUE ASHWORTH

SIMON &
SCHUSTER
ILLUSTRATED

London · New York · Sydney · Toronto · New Delhi

A CBS COMPANY

The Recipes

 ProPoints values: You'll find a *ProPoints* value beside every recipe in this book. This tells you how many *ProPoints* values per serving each recipe contains.

Filling & Healthy Foods: We highlight all of our Filling & Healthy foods in green. These foods are at the heart of our plan so eat them where you can – they will help to fill you up faster and keep you fuller for longer. If you are on a Filling & Healthy day approach look at the handy box on each recipe that tells you how many of your weekly 49 *ProPoints* allowance you'll need to use. Watch out though – they have been calculated per serving; if you have more than one serving you may need to use more of your weekly *ProPoints* allowance.

V This means the recipe is suitable for vegetarians. Where relevant, free-range eggs, vegetarian cheese, vegetarian virtually fat-free fromage frais, vegetarian low fat crème fraîche and vegetarian low fat yogurts are used. Virtually fat-free fromage frais, low fat crème fraîche and low fat yogurts may contain traces of gelatine so they are not always suitable for a vegetarian diet – just check the labels.

❄ This means you can freeze this dish. There may be specific freezing instructions so just check the recipe to be sure.

The small print

Eggs We use medium eggs, unless otherwise stated. Pregnant women, the elderly and children should avoid recipes with eggs which are not fully cooked or raw.

Fruit and Vegetables Our recipes use medium-sized fruit and veg unless otherwise stated.

Chocolate We use chocolate with a minimum of 70% cocoa solids.

Low fat spread When a recipe uses a low fat spread, we mean a spread with a fat content of 40%.

Microwaves If we have used a microwave in any of our recipes, the timings will be for an 850 watt microwave oven.

Prep and Cooking Times These are approximate and meant to be guidelines. Prep time includes all the steps up to and following the main cooking time(s).

Low fat soft cheese Where a recipe uses low fat soft cheese, we mean a soft cheese with a fat content of 3% or less.

First published in Great Britain by Simon & Schuster UK Ltd, 2014
A CBS Company

Copyright © 2014, Weight Watchers International, Inc.

SIMON & SCHUSTER
ILLUSTRATED BOOKS
Simon & Schuster UK Ltd
222 Gray's Inn Road
London WC1X 8HB
www.simonandschuster.co.uk
Simon & Schuster Australia, Sydney
Simon & Schuster India, New Delhi

This book is copyright under the Berne Convention.
No reproduction without permission.
All rights reserved.

10 9 8 7 6 5 4 3 2 1

Weight Watchers, *ProPoints* and the *ProPoints* icon are the registered trademarks of Weight Watchers International Inc. and used under license by Weight Watchers (UK) Ltd. All rights reserved.

Weight Watchers Publications Team:
Imogen Prescott, Nina McKerlie
Photography: William Shaw
Food stylist: Sue Ashworth
Prop styling: Jenny Iggleden

For Simon & Schuster Illustrated
Director of Illustrated Publishing:
Ami Stewart
Senior Commissioning Editor: Nicky Hill
Art Director: Corinna Farrow
Production Manager: Katherine Thornton
Design: Miranda Harvey

Colour Reproduction by
Dot Gradations Ltd, UK
Printed and bound in Germany

A CIP catalogue record for this book is available from the British Library

ISBN: 978-1-47113-463-0

Pictured on front cover, clockwise from top left: Squidgy carrot cake, page 190; Fish finger sarnie, page 124; Ultimate red Thai chicken curry, page 58; Roast loin of pork with a rosemary and thyme crust, page 64
Pictured on back cover from left to right: Steak and pepper goulash, page 130; Macaroni cauliflower cheese, page 76; Fresh berry sponge, page 210
Pictured on back flap: Home-made turkey burger, page 56

CONTENTS

INTRODUCING
The Author

I've been *Cooking the Weight Watchers Way* for over 20 years now, and I can honestly say that I've felt the benefits in so many ways.

As a cookery writer and food stylist, you'd think it would be hard to keep control of my weight when every day I'm surrounded by lovely food. It's a delicious part of my job to test and taste. I have, however, had my moments when the scales have tipped in the wrong direction, but Weight Watchers always catches hold of me and pulls me back in when I start to flounder. Over the years, Weight Watchers has proved to be the eating plan that I can rely on – and, yes, I'm a Gold Member so I know how good it feels to keep on track.

I do hope you'll embrace *Cooking the Weight Watchers Way* and love the great recipes contained within these pages. I've spent time working with the Weight Watchers team to come up with dishes that you, the member, will love and need – and that will make your life a whole lot easier. There are recipes for when time is short; good old classic recipes that you'll use over and over; recipes that are all zero ***ProPoints*** values for when you'd rather not use up any of your budget; recipes that you just can't live without; and, of course, there's a whole chapter of guilt-free treat recipes. Trust me, the food is all very tasty – and you certainly won't go hungry!

I really hope you enjoy cooking the recipes in this book as much as I enjoyed writing them. And to know that they helped you on your journey would make me very happy!

All the best

Sue Ashworth

WEIGHT WATCHERS
and the ProPoints plan

Food is our fuel, and it's all around us every day. It's time to put yourself back in control of the food choices you make. Weight Watchers gives you a plan to help you achieve this and you can adapt the plan according to your personal preference – whether you want to take a simple approach or a more flexible approach, the choice is yours.

How this cookbook can work best for you: no matter where you are in your journey

Whether you're on a Filling & Healthy day approach or you've moved to ultimate flexibility and are counting everything, this cookbook will tell you exactly how much of your weekly or daily *ProPoints* allowance you will need to use to make each recipe.

Filling & Healthy Day Approach

If you're on a Filling & Healthy day each recipe clearly indicates how many of your weekly 49 *ProPoints* values you'll need to use – just take a look at the box below every recipe. This takes into account all of those foods that aren't on the Filling & Healthy food list and gives you a *ProPoints* value for those foods alone. This makes it really easy for you to cook and enjoy these recipes.

Fully Flexible Counting Day

If you are counting everything, you will see on the recipe itself exactly how many *ProPoints* values you will need to use from your daily *ProPoints* allowance. This makes it really easy to follow the plan while cooking from scratch as there is no guesswork involved.

Quick ProPoints values index

Zero Heroes

The Classics

Point Stretchers

Comfort Food

Quick Fixes

Guilt-free Treats

 Super-berry blitz **16**

 Zero hero soup **18**

 Carrot and ginger soup **20**

 Hampshire watercress soup **22**

 Griddled pepper and tomato salad **24**

 Char-grilled asparagus salad **26**

 Fennel, rocket and red grapefruit salad **28**

 Mega-veg steam fry **32**

 Roast butternut wedges with chilli and cumin **34**

 Spiced roast vegetables **36**

 Cauliflower, squash and spinach curry **38**

 Thai vegetable bowl **40**

 Baked nectarines with summer berries **42**

 Perfectly posh jellies **44**

 Poached autumn fruits **46**

 Cumin-spiced cauliflower and squash **84**

Griddled courgettes with feta and peas **98**

Ham, leek and red pepper tarts **106**

Marvellous minestrone **114**

Creamy vegetable soup **116**

2 ProPoints value

Strawberry mousse with smashed amaretti **206**

3 ProPoints value

Chicken, leek and barley broth **90**

3 ProPoints value

Carrot, cumin and red lentil dip **92**

3 ProPoints value

Crispbread toppers: Cottage cheese and Marmite **100**

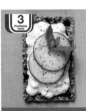
3 ProPoints value

Spiced summer veg supper **168**

3 ProPoints value

Muesli morning munchies **218**

4 ProPoints value

Asian prawn noodle salad **94**

4 ProPoints value

Crispbread toppers: Tuna and cucumber **100**

4 ProPoints value

Leek and potato soup **118**

4 ProPoints value

Cauliflower cheese soup **152**

4 ProPoints value

Allotment frittata **166**

4 ProPoints value

Chocolate sponge puddings **188**

4 ProPoints value

Cappuccino crèmes **192**

4 ProPoints value

Strawberry and apple crumbles **194**

4 ProPoints value

Plum beautiful tarts **196**

4 ProPoints value

Mango, kiwi and raspberry knickerbocker glories **208**

5 ProPoints value

Ham and asparagus rolls **86**

5 ProPoints value

Two-potato salad **86**

5 ProPoints value

Grilled fish with tomatoes, lemon and chives **88**

5 ProPoints value

Crispbread toppers: Curried chicken and mango **100**

5 ProPoints value

Crispbread toppers: Lemon curd and banana **100**

5 ProPoints value

Baked potato fillers: Feta with cucumber and tomato salsa **102**

5 ProPoints value

Couscous and quinoa salad **104**

5 ProPoints value

Baked aubergine Parmigiana **120**

5 ProPoints value

Garden pitta pizzas **146**

5 ProPoints value

Houmous and carrot salad bruschetta **154**

5 ProPoints value

Mexican salsa melts **156**

5 ProPoints value

Grilled haddock with prawn and Cheddar topping **178**

5 ProPoints value

Tuna, red onion and mixed bean lunch **182**

Squidgy carrot cake **190**

Quick ProPoints values index

5 ProPoints value
Orange and choc-olate chip bread and butter pudding **202**

5 ProPoints value
Apple and black-berry cheesecake sundaes **204**

5 ProPoints value
Fresh berry sponge **210**

5 ProPoints value
Banana cake **212**

5 ProPoints value
Strawberry and lemon butterfly cakes **214**

6 ProPoints value
Weight Watchers all-day breakfast **50**

6 ProPoints value
Country cottage pie **52**

6 ProPoints value
Asparagus, cour-gette and plum tomato pasta **96**

6 ProPoints value
Steak and pepper goulash **130**

6 ProPoints value
Sea bass with fennel, orange and cannellini beans **148**

6 ProPoints value
Quick beef and pepper noodles **176**

6 ProPoints value
Wasabi smoked salmon wraps **180**

6 ProPoints value
Little chocolate pots **186**

6 ProPoints value
Hot lemon sauce puddings **198**

6 ProPoints value
Spiced cranberry and banana muffins **216**

7 ProPoints value
Home-made turkey burger **56**

7 ProPoints value
Tortilla, tomato and aubergine stack **108**

Fish finger sarnie **124**

7 ProPoints value
Potato and onion hotpot with crispy bacon **142**

7 ProPoints value
Bacon, egg and tomato salad **162**

8 ProPoints value
Roasted vegetable lasagne **72**

8 ProPoints value
Veggie spag bol **78**

8 ProPoints value
Sweet chilli duck with sesame noodles **82**

8 ProPoints value
Midweek chicken roast **110**

8 ProPoints value
Orzo pasta and ham salad **150**

8 ProPoints value
Curried lamb pittas with coriander raita **160**

8 ProPoints value
Gnocchi with roasted peppers, peas and Parmesan **170**

9 ProPoints value
Lamb and apricot tagine **66**

9 ProPoints value
Macaroni cauliflower cheese **76**

9 ProPoints value
Baked potato fillers: Curried chicken **102**

Baked potato fillers: Spicy beans and peppers **102**

Leek, pea and parsley risotto **122**

Spring lamb stew **134**

Ramen noodles with chilli and chicken **136**

Chicken fusilli **158**

Moroccan-spiced turkey steaks **174**

Chilli con carne **54**

Ultimate red Thai chicken curry **58**

Chicken pasanda **60**

Chicken casserole with sage and onion dumplings **62**

Roast loin of pork with a rosemary and thyme crust **64**

Classic fish pie **68**

Perfect prawn biriyani **70**

Potato and aubergine moussaka **74**

Grilled lemon salmon with leek and caper mash **126**

Pork saltimbocca **132**

Chicken schnitzel **138**

Sausage, egg, chips and baked beans **140**

Hot roast chicken salad **172**

Zero Heroes

The Classics

Point Stretchers

Comfort Food

Quick Fixes

Guilt-free Treats

"*Always keep a full and varied fruit bowl!* I CAN'T STRESS ENOUGH HOW MUCH IT HELPS TO HAVE THOSE ZERO PROPOINTS VALUE SNACKS TO HAND!"

Dawn Williamson Weight Watchers member

ZERO Heroes

PROPOINTS VALUES

SUPER-BERRY
Blitz

You can enjoy a healthy fresh fruit smoothie at any time of the day – it's the perfect fill-me-up treat that won't use up any of your *ProPoints* values.

 ProPoints values per serving
ProPoints values per recipe 0

 Serves 4
Takes 3 minutes

200 g (7 oz) blueberries
200 g (7 oz) strawberries
200 g (7 oz) raspberries (fresh or frozen)
2 bananas, sliced
1 teaspoon vanilla extract
425 ml (15 fl oz) chilled water

1 Put all the ingredients into a blender or food processor and blitz for 15–20 seconds until smooth, or use a hand-held blender.

2 Pour into glasses and serve immediately.

Cook's tips Adjust the amount of water to achieve the consistency you prefer.

Try to get into the habit of making smoothies regularly, as they are a great way to enjoy fresh fruit. Encourage the kids to drink them too, and get them to help make them.

Variations Mango, banana and strawberry; papaya, lime juice and raspberry; blueberry, blackberry and banana – the combinations are endless. Try using frozen fruit too – there's no need to thaw it before blending.

Following the Filling & Healthy day approach? You don't need to use any of your weekly *ProPoints* allowance for a serving of this recipe.

ProPoints values to spare?

+1 per portion by blitzing 2 x 60 g (2 oz) scoops of low fat ice cream with the fruits.

+1 per portion by blending 2 x 150 g pots of virtually fat free natural yogurt with the fruits.

+2 per portion by blitzing 80 g (3 oz) of low sugar muesli with the fruits to make a breakfast smoothie.

ZERO HERO
Soup

Packed to the brim with good-for-you vegetables, this soup will soon be one of your favourite zero heroes, keeping you feeling full and satisfied throughout the day.

ProPoints values per serving
ProPoints values per recipe 1

Serves 6
Takes 35 minutes

2 vegetable stock cubes
1 large **onion**, chopped
1 large **courgette**, cubed
2 large **carrots**, cubed
1 **turnip**, cubed
1 **leek**, sliced
2 **celery** sticks, sliced thinly
1 tablespoon chopped **fresh parsley**
1 teaspoon dried mixed herbs
salt and freshly ground black pepper

1 Crumble the stock cubes into a large lidded saucepan and add 1.5 litres (2¾ pints) water. Bring up to the boil, stirring occasionally.

2 Add the onion, courgette, carrots, turnip, leek and celery. Stir in the parsley and dried herbs. Bring back to the boil, then reduce the heat and simmer, partially covered, for 20–25 minutes, until the vegetables are tender.

3 Season to taste, then serve. Cool any leftover soup as quickly as possible, then store in the fridge in a covered container for up to 4 days, reheating thoroughly when required.

Cook's tip If you prefer, make a smooth soup by blending in a food processor, or use a hand-held blender to purée the soup in the saucepan. Alternatively, just partially blend the soup, so that it still has some vegetable chunks in it.

Variations Use 4 or 5 **shallots** instead of the onion, if you like, and try dried mixed Italian herbs instead.

Following the Filling & Healthy day approach? You don't need to use any of your weekly *ProPoints* allowance for a serving of this recipe.

ProPoints values to spare?

+1 by serving each portion with 2 teaspoons (10 g) finely grated Parmesan cheese.

+2 by serving each portion with a 30 g (1¼ oz) mini pitta bread, white or wholemeal.

+3 by serving each portion with a 50 g (1¾ oz) brown, granary or wholemeal roll.

CARROT AND GINGER
Soup

Simple and cheap to make, with very few ingredients, the ginger in this soup offsets the sweetness of the carrots, complementing them perfectly.

 ProPoints values per serving
ProPoints values per recipe 2

  Serves 6
Takes 35 minutes

500 g (1 lb 2 oz) carrots, chopped
1 large garlic clove, crushed
2 onions, chopped
2 vegetable stock cubes
1 tablespoon tomato purée
2 teaspoons finely grated fresh root
    ginger (or 1 teaspoon ground)
salt and freshly ground black pepper
fresh parsley sprigs, to garnish

1 Put the carrots, garlic and onions into a large lidded saucepan and add 1.5 litres (2¾ pints) water. Crumble in the vegetable stock cubes. Bring up to the boil, stirring occasionally.

2 Stir in the tomato purée and add the grated or ground ginger. Reduce the heat and simmer, partially covered, for 20–25 minutes, until the carrots are tender.

3 Transfer the soup to a blender or food processor and blend until smooth. Alternatively, use a hand-held blender to purée the soup in the saucepan. Season to taste, adding a little more ginger if needed, then reheat and serve, sprinkled with extra black pepper and garnished with parsley.

4 Cool any leftover soup as quickly as possible, then store in the fridge in a covered container for up to 4 days, reheating thoroughly when required.

Following the Filling & Healthy day approach? You don't need to use any of your weekly *ProPoints* allowance for a serving of this recipe.

ProPoints values to spare?

+1 per portion by adding 150 g (5½ oz) low fat soft cheese to the soup when blending it, to give a fabulously creamy taste and texture.

+1 by topping each portion with 2 tablespoons of low fat Greek yogurt.

+2 by serving each portion with a 30 g (1¼ oz) slice of brown, granary, white or wholemeal bread.

HAMPSHIRE WATERCRESS
Soup

One of my favourite salad leaves grows in abundance in Hampshire – and it makes the most marvellous soup. Serve it piping hot or try it icy cold in summer.

ProPoints values per serving
ProPoints values per recipe 1

Serves 4
Takes 30 minutes

2 **onions**, chopped
1 large **garlic clove**, crushed
1 vegetable stock cube
150 g (5½ oz) **watercress**, chopped roughly, stalks included
a small handful of **fresh parsley**, chopped roughly
salt and freshly ground black pepper
watercress sprigs, to garnish

1 Put the onions and garlic into a large lidded saucepan and add 1.2 litres (2 pints) of water. Crumble in the vegetable stock cube. Bring up to the boil, stirring occasionally.

2 Reduce the heat and simmer, partially covered, for 15–20 minutes, until the onions are tender.

3 Reserve a few sprigs of watercress for garnish, then add the rest to the saucepan with the parsley. Cook for another 3–4 minutes, until wilted.

4 Transfer the soup to a blender or food processor and blend until smooth. Alternatively, use a hand-held blender to purée the soup in the saucepan. Season to taste, then reheat and serve, garnished with watercress sprigs.

5 Cool any leftover soup as quickly as possible, then store in the fridge in a covered container for up to 4 days, reheating thoroughly when required.

Cook's tip If serving chilled, make sure that the soup is refrigerated for several hours or overnight so that it's icy cold. Serve in chilled bowls, with an ice cube dropped into each portion just before serving.

Following the Filling & Healthy day approach? You don't need to use any of your weekly **ProPoints** allowance for a serving of this recipe.

ProPoints values to spare?

+1 by swirling ½ tablespoon of single cream on to each portion before serving.

+2 by serving each portion with a 40 g (1½ oz) slice of brown Irish soda bread or a mini 30 g (1¼ oz) pitta.

GRIDDLED PEPPER
and Tomato Salad

Fuel up your body with vitamin C by enjoying this bright and beautiful salad.

ProPoints values per serving
ProPoints values per recipe 0

Serves 4
Takes 30 minutes

2 large red or yellow peppers, halved
    and de-seeded
1 small red onion, sliced thinly
3 tablespoons red or white wine
    vinegar
a large bag of mixed salad leaves
1 beef tomato, sliced
4 plum tomatoes, sliced
12 cherry tomatoes, halved
salt and freshly ground black pepper
fresh basil or oregano leaves, to
    garnish (optional)

1 Preheat the grill. Arrange the pepper halves, skin side up, on the grill rack. Grill for 8–10 minutes, or until the skins are blackened and charred. Switch off the grill, leaving the peppers in the grill compartment with the door closed. The steamy atmosphere will loosen their skins. If you don't have a separate grill compartment, put the peppers into a bowl and cover with a lid or cling film and leave until cool – about 15 minutes.

2 Meanwhile, put the onion into a bowl and add the vinegar. Season with a little salt and plenty of black pepper, and leave to marinate for 10–15 minutes.

3 Share the salad leaves between 4 serving plates and top each one with an equal amount of the different tomato varieties. Peel the cooled peppers, and tear up half a pepper over each salad, mixing the colours if using red and yellow.

4 Spoon the softened onions and vinegar over the salads and finish off with a few basil or oregano leaves, if using. Serve sprinkled with a little extra black pepper.

Cook's tip You don't have to use three varieties of tomato, just use your favourite.

Following the Filling & Healthy day approach? You don't need to use any of your weekly **ProPoints** allowance for a serving of this recipe.

ProPoints values to spare?

+1 by sprinkling each salad with 1 tablespoon ready-made croûtons.

+1 by serving each portion with 2 teaspoons finely shaved Parmesan cheese.

CHAR-GRILLED ASPARAGUS
Salad

When you char-grill asparagus, you add lots of flavour and that is what gives this salad a really great taste.

ProPoints values per serving 0
ProPoints values per recipe 0

V Serves 4
Takes 25 minutes

300 g (10½ oz) fine asparagus
1 teaspoon Dijon mustard
1 tablespoon hot water
finely grated zest and juice of
    1 lemon
2 Romaine lettuces, shredded
12 cherry tomatoes, halved
2 roasted red peppers from a jar,
    packed in brine
100 g (3½ oz) radishes, sliced
4 spring onions, finely chopped
salt and freshly ground black pepper
fresh flat leaf parsley or basil, to
    garnish (optional)

1 Preheat a char-grill pan or the grill. Char-grill or grill the asparagus (in batches, if necessary) for 6–8 minutes, or until tender and evenly cooked.

2 In a large salad bowl, mix together the mustard, hot water, lemon zest and juice. Season with a pinch of salt and plenty of black pepper. Add the lettuce and tomatoes, tossing to coat. Share between 4 serving plates.

3 Rip up the red peppers and share them between the salads, then add the asparagus spears. Scatter the radishes and spring onions over the top, then serve each portion garnished with flat leaf parsley or a few basil leaves, if using.

Cook's tip Make the most of fresh English asparagus when it's at its seasonal best in May and June.

Variation You can use courgettes, sliced lengthways, instead of asparagus – they char-grill beautifully.

Following the Filling & Healthy day approach? You don't need to use any of your weekly **ProPoints** allowance for a serving of this recipe.

ProPoints values to spare?

+1 per portion by adding 2 teaspoons of olive oil to the salad dressing.

+1 by adding 10 olives in brine to each portion.

+2 per portion by crumbling 100 g (3½ oz) feta cheese and sharing it between the salads.

FENNEL, ROCKET
and Red Grapefruit Salad

Simple, yet inspired. Enjoy this salad as a refreshing side dish or serve it for a light summer lunch.

 ProPoints values per serving
ProPoints values per recipe 0

 Serves 2
Takes 15 minutes

1 bulb fennel, sliced thinly
2 red grapefruit
100 g (3½ oz) rocket leaves
1 tablespoon chopped fresh dill or
    chives
freshly ground black pepper

1 Put the fennel into a large salad bowl. Using a sharp, serrated knife, peel the grapefruit over the bowl to catch the juice, removing all the peel and pith. Slice the grapefruit, removing all the pith from each segment. Toss the segments gently with the fennel and leave for a few minutes.

2 Arrange the rocket on 2 serving plates. Pile the fennel and grapefruit mixture on top, then serve sprinkled with the dill or chives and seasoned with black pepper.

Cook's tip Use a sawing action with a serrated knife to remove the peel and pith cleanly.

Variation If you're not keen on the slightly aniseed flavour of fennel, try char-grilled courgettes or asparagus instead.

Following the Filling & Healthy day approach? You don't need to use any of your weekly *ProPoints* allowance for a serving of this recipe.

ProPoints values to spare?

+1 by serving a 2.5 cm (1 inch) slice of French stick with each portion.

+2 by sharing ½ a medium avocado between the two salads.

+3 by crumbling 40 g (1½ oz) feta cheese over each portion.

"*My mandolin slicer* cost me next to nothing from the supermarket and has easily doubled my veg intake, most of which is a nice big zero *ProPoints* values. Everything sliced nice and thin super quick for omelettes, ratatouille, you name it, I slice it!"

Emma Barrow Weight Watchers member

"AS A BUSY MUM I FIND THAT IT HELPS MY WEIGHT LOSS WHEN I MAKE UP THREE LARGE TUPPERWARE TUBS IN THE FRIDGE: ONE WITH SALAD, ONE WITH EITHER ROASTED VEG OR SOUP, AND ONE WITH FRUIT SALAD. IT MAKES IT EASIER FOR ME WHEN I COOK AS ALL THE ZERO PROPOINTS VALUE FOODS ARE ALL READY-PREPARED."

Ginny Lidstone Weight Watchers member

"I USE
CAULIFLOWER
INSTEAD OF RICE
AND COURGETTE
STRIPS RATHER
THAN PASTA."

Cat Woods
Weight Watchers member

Zero ProPoints value Ratatouille

"When there's an abundance of seasonal veg going cheap I make this ratatouille using marrow or courgette, peppers, onion, garlic, carrots, celery, any other veg lurking in the fridge, a couple of cans of chopped tomatoes and fresh bay leaves from my tree in the garden. Mix it up, cover with foil and bake for an hour or so. Freeze in portion sizes and then defrost. Use to cover chicken breasts, pork loin steaks, cod or salmon fillets and bake until your meat or fish is cooked. Serve with rice or a jacket spud."

Emma Saville Weight Watchers member

MEGA-VEG
Steam Fry

This recipe is a cross between stir-frying and steaming, meaning you get a delicious, vitamin-packed meal – without using any *ProPoints* values.

 ProPoints values per serving
ProPoints values per recipe 1

 Serves 2
Takes 15 minutes

calorie controlled cooking spray
1 large carrot, cut into fine strips
1 red or yellow pepper, de-seeded
    and cut into fine strips
4 spring onions, thinly sliced
200 g (7 oz) baby corn, halved
100 g (3½ oz) sugarsnap peas or
    mangetout, halved
1 small green chilli, de-seeded and
    sliced thinly (optional)
½ small Savoy or white cabbage,
    shredded
finely grated zest of 1 small orange
2 tablespoons soy sauce
½ teaspoon Chinese five spice
    powder

1 Heat a wok over a high heat and spray with the cooking spray. Add the carrot, pepper, spring onions, baby corn, sugarsnap peas or mangetout, and chilli (if using). Stir-fry for 3–4 minutes.

2 Add the cabbage and a splash of water to the wok. Continue to cook and stir for another 2–3 minutes, until the cabbage is cooked, yet still crunchy.

3 Add the orange zest, soy sauce and Chinese five spice powder and stir everything together for a few more moments. Share between 2 warmed plates or bowls and serve at once.

Cook's tip When grating zest, be sure to use only the coloured part – the white pith tastes bitter.

Variations Use Chinese leaf lettuce instead of cabbage, and broccoli florets instead of sugarsnap peas or mangetout.

Following the Filling & Healthy day approach? You don't need to use any of your weekly *ProPoints* allowance for a serving of this recipe.

ProPoints values to spare?

+1 per portion by stirring 2 tablespoons of sweet chilli sauce into the wok with the soy sauce.

+3 by sharing 150 g (5½ oz) cooked egg noodles between the two portions.

ROAST BUTTERNUT WEDGES
with Chilli and Cumin

Roast butternut squash is so satisfying; its sweet flesh is offset perfectly by chilli and cumin seeds. A delicious hot snack for the chillier months – and a great side dish, too.

 ProPoints values per serving **0**
ProPoints values per recipe 1

 Serves 4
Takes 40 minutes

1 small **butternut squash**, de-seeded and cut into wedges
calorie controlled cooking spray
1 teaspoon chilli flakes
1 teaspoon cumin seeds
salt and freshly ground black pepper

1 Preheat the oven to Gas Mark 6/200°C/fan oven 180°C.

2 Arrange the butternut squash in a large roasting tin and spray with 2 sprays of the cooking spray. Bake in the oven for 25 minutes.

3 Turn the butternut squash wedges, then sprinkle them with the chilli flakes and cumin seeds. Season with a little salt and black pepper. Return to the oven for a further 10–15 minutes, until the wedges are tender (check with a sharp knife to make sure).

Cook's tip Butternut squash can be quite hard to slice, so use a good sharp cook's knife. There's no need to peel it: when you eat it you can just scoop the soft flesh from the skin and, in fact, the skin is edible, so you can eat it too. You can buy ready-prepared butternut squash, though you'll pay a little extra for it.

Variation Use a thinly sliced de-seeded fresh **chilli** instead of the chilli flakes or, if you're not keen on chilli, just leave it out altogether.

Following the Filling & Healthy day approach? You don't need to use any of your weekly **ProPoints** allowance for a serving of this recipe.

ProPoints values to spare?

+3 per portion for non-vegetarians by sprinkling 125 g (4½ oz) finely chopped chorizo sausage over the squash when you add the chilli and cumin.

SPICED ROAST
Vegetables

A true zero hero. Serve on its own for a hearty filler, enjoy warm over mixed leaves with a lemon and fresh herb dressing, or purée with vegetable stock to make a tasty soup.

ProPoints values per serving
ProPoints values per recipe 0

V Serves 4
Takes 40 minutes

300 g (10½ oz) **butternut squash**, peeled, de-seeded and cut into chunks
300 g (10½ oz) Chantenay or small **carrots**, scrubbed and halved
calorie controlled cooking spray
1 large **courgette**, sliced
1 yellow and 1 red **pepper**, de-seeded and cut into chunks
1 **red onion**, cut into thin wedges
1 teaspoon Cajun seasoning
a few sprigs of **fresh thyme**
12 cherry **tomatoes**
salt and freshly ground black pepper

1 Preheat the oven to Gas Mark 6/200°C/fan oven 180°C.

2 Tip the butternut squash and carrots into a large roasting tin and spray with the cooking spray, tossing to coat lightly. Roast in the oven for 15 minutes.

3 Add the courgette, peppers and red onion to the roasting tin. Sprinkle with the Cajun seasoning and stir to mix thoroughly. Scatter the thyme sprigs on top and return to the oven to continue roasting for another 20 minutes, or until the vegetables are tender.

4 Add the cherry tomatoes to the roasting tin, season, and roast for 5 more minutes.

Cook's tip Butternut squash and carrots take longer to cook, that's why it's best to add the other veg later, so they don't overcook. But there's nothing to stop you from putting all the vegetables into the roasting tin at once – especially if you're busy.

Following the Filling & Healthy day approach? You don't need to use any of your weekly **ProPoints** allowance for a serving of this recipe.

ProPoints values to spare?

+3 by serving each portion with a 40 g (1½ oz) soft tortilla.

CAULIFLOWER, SQUASH
and Spinach Curry

A bowlful of this vegetable curry will fill you up a treat. It's one of my favourites for a Friday curry night.

 ProPoints values per serving
ProPoints values per recipe 2

 Serves 4
Takes 35 minutes

2 teaspoons ground coriander
2 teaspoons cumin seeds
½ teaspoon ground turmeric
½ vegetable stock cube
1 tablespoon tomato purée
1 green chilli, de-seeded and sliced thinly
400 g (14 oz) butternut squash, peeled, de-seeded and cut into chunks
400 g (14 oz) carrots, sliced
1 onion, chopped
1 cauliflower, broken into florets
100 g (3½ oz) baby spinach
salt and freshly ground black pepper

1 Put the ground coriander, cumin seeds and turmeric into a large lidded saucepan and heat for 1–2 minutes to lightly toast the spices and bring out their flavour, taking care not to burn them.

2 Dissolve the vegetable stock cube in 1 litre (1¾ pints) boiling water. Add the vegetable stock, tomato purée and chilli. Tip in the squash, carrots and onion. Bring to the boil, then reduce the heat and simmer for 15 minutes, partially covered.

3 Add the cauliflower to the saucepan and cook for a further 8–10 minutes, until the cauliflower is tender, but not too soft. At this point add the spinach and cook for a further 2–3 minutes to wilt the leaves. Season, then serve.

Variation Use 2 tablespoons of medium curry powder instead of the ground coriander, cumin and turmeric.

Following the Filling & Healthy day approach? You don't need to use any of your weekly *ProPoints* allowance for a serving of this recipe.

ProPoints values to spare?

+3 by roughly chopping 50 g (1¾ oz) salted peanuts and sharing between the portions.

+3 by serving each portion with a Weight Watchers mini naan bread.

THAI VEGETABLE
Bowl

Fragrant Thai spices give these vegetables a wonderful flavour, making them a meal in their own right.

 ProPoints values per serving
ProPoints values per recipe 1

Serves 4
Takes 25 minutes

1 litre (1¾ pints) vegetable stock
2 tablespoons Thai fish sauce
1 lemongrass stalk, bashed with a
   rolling pin
2–3 dried kaffir lime leaves
1 tablespoon finely grated fresh root
   ginger
2 garlic cloves, crushed
1 red chilli, de-seeded and finely
   sliced
8 shallots, halved
150 g (5½ oz) mangetout or
   sugarsnap peas, halved
200 g (7 oz) tenderstem broccoli, cut
   into short lengths
1 yellow and 1 red pepper,
   de-seeded and sliced into strips
150 g (5½ oz) mushrooms, sliced
2 heads of pak choi, separated into
   leaves

1 Put the vegetable stock, fish sauce, lemongrass, lime leaves, ginger, garlic, chilli and shallots into a large lidded saucepan. Slowly bring up to the boil over a low heat.

2 Add all the remaining vegetables to the saucepan, apart from the pak choi. Simmer, partially covered, for 8–10 minutes. Finally, add the pak choi and simmer for another 2–3 minutes to wilt the leaves.

3 Ladle the vegetables and broth into warmed bowls and serve.

Cook's tip Don't overcook the vegetables; they should remain bright and crisp.

Following the Filling & Healthy day approach? You don't need to use any of your weekly **ProPoints** allowance for a serving of this recipe.

BAKED NECTARINES
with Summer Berries

Enjoy this baked fruit dish when summer berries are at their best. It's a great way to round off a meal, without spending any extra *ProPoints* values.

 ProPoints values per serving
ProPoints values per recipe 0

 Serves 4
Takes 25 minutes

4 ripe nectarines, halved and stoned
strips of zest from a lemon
2 teaspoons vanilla extract
200 g (7 oz) strawberries, halved
125 g (4½ oz) raspberries
100 g (3½ oz) blueberries

1 Preheat the oven to Gas Mark 5/190°C/fan oven 170°C.

2 Arrange the nectarines in a baking dish with the cut sides facing upwards. Add 150 ml (5 fl oz) water to a saucepan with the lemon zest and simmer for 5 minutes. Remove the zest and add the vanilla extract, then spoon the liquid over the nectarines. Bake for 10 minutes.

3 Scatter the strawberries, raspberries and blueberries over the nectarines and bake for 5 more minutes. Serve while warm.

Cook's tips For the best flavour, make sure the nectarines are properly ripe.

Use a potato peeler to pare thin strips of lemon zest.

Variations Try orange zest instead of lemon, and peaches instead of nectarines. You can also use frozen summer berries – just bake the dish for 1–2 minutes longer.

Following the Filling & Healthy day approach? You don't need to use any of your weekly *ProPoints* allowance for a serving of this recipe.

ProPoints values to spare?

+1 by serving each portion with 1 tablespoon of half fat crème fraîche.

+3 by serving each portion with a 60 g (2 oz) scoop of vanilla ice cream.

PERFECTLY POSH
Jellies

You can transform fresh fruit into a really posh dessert if you set it in jelly.

 ProPoints values per serving
ProPoints values per recipe 1

Serves 4
Takes 20 minutes
+ 2–3 hours setting

1 large ripe mango, peeled, stoned
  and chopped into chunks
250 g (9 oz) raspberries
23 g sachet raspberry sugar-free jelly
300 ml (10 fl oz) just-boiled water
juice of 1 lime
lime wedges, to decorate (optional)

1 Spoon the mango chunks and raspberries into 4 serving glasses.

2 Sprinkle the jelly crystals into the just-boiled water, stirring until dissolved. Add the lime juice, then make the mixture up to 500 ml (18 fl oz) with cold water. Pour it into the glasses and transfer to the fridge to set – about 2–3 hours.

3 When ready to serve, decorate the jellies with the lime wedges (if using).

Cook's tip Remember that the gelatine in regular jelly crystals isn't suitable for vegetarians. Always buy the vegetarian version when catering for vegetarians.

Variations Try combinations such as strawberries and orange, or cherries and banana. One thing to note is that fresh pineapple, papaya and kiwi fruit aren't suitable substitutes, as they contain an enzyme that stops the jelly setting.

Following the Filling & Healthy day approach? You don't need to use any of your weekly *ProPoints* allowance for a serving of this recipe.

ProPoints values to spare?

+**1** by topping each jelly with 1 tablespoon of half fat crème fraîche.

+**2** by whipping 4 tablespoons of double cream until thick, and sharing it between the jellies.

+**3** by serving each jelly with a 60 g (2 oz) scoop of vanilla ice cream.

POACHED AUTUMN
Fruits

Celebrate the turn of the season with the spicy flavours of this lovely warm fruit salad.

 ProPoints values per serving
ProPoints values per recipe 2

 Serves 4
Takes 30 minutes

4 just-ripe pears, peeled
finely grated zest and juice of 1 small
    orange
1 cinnamon stick (or ¼ teaspoon
    ground cinnamon)
4 cloves (or pinch of ground cloves)
1 teaspoon vanilla extract
250 g (9 oz) blackberries
4 large or 6 small plums, halved and
    pitted

1 Stand the pears in a saucepan with the orange zest and juice. Add enough water to come about three-quarters of the way up their sides, then add the cinnamon stick, cloves, vanilla extract and half the blackberries. Simmer gently for 15 minutes, without a lid, turning the pears occasionally.

2 Add the plums to the saucepan and cook for a further 10–12 minutes. Check that the pears are tender with the point of a sharp knife. Remove from the heat and stir in the remaining blackberries. Leave to cool slightly, but serve the pears while still warm.

3 To serve, remove the cinnamon stick and cloves from the cooking liquid. Slice each pear in half and remove the core with a melon baller or sharp knife. Slicing the pears reveals the colour that they absorb while cooking with the blackberries. Share the warm fruit between 4 serving bowls.

Cook's tip Don't choose pears that are too ripe, or they will go mushy when cooked.

Following the Filling & Healthy day approach? You don't need to use any of your weekly *ProPoints* allowance for a serving of this recipe.

ProPoints values to spare?

+1 by drizzling 1 teaspoon of clear honey over each portion.

+2 by serving each portion with a 60 g (2 oz) scoop of low fat ice cream.

+3 by serving each portion with a 150 g pot of low fat ready-to-serve custard.

"*My slow cooker is a must;* I CHUCK ALL THE VEG AND MEAT IN FIRST THING IN THE MORNING AND SET IT TO GO. THAT WAY THERE IS NO EXCUSE FOR NOT HAVING *a healthy low ProPoints value meal ready when you need it,* NO MATTER HOW BUSY YOU ARE."

Victoria Simmons Weight Watchers member

The CLASSICS

PROPOINTS VALUES

WEIGHT WATCHERS
All-Day Breakfast

Nothing quite beats the appeal of an all-day breakfast. Here's how to enjoy it Weight Watchers style – without blowing your *ProPoints* budget.

 6 *ProPoints* values per serving
ProPoints values per recipe 23

Serves 4
Takes 20 minutes

300 g (10 oz) mushrooms, sliced
150 ml (5 fl oz) vegetable stock
420 g can reduced sugar and salt
    baked beans
4 rashers lean back bacon
4 tomatoes, halved
calorie controlled cooking spray
4 eggs
freshly ground black pepper

1 Preheat the grill. Put the mushrooms and stock into a large saucepan. Bring up to the boil, then reduce the heat and simmer for 5–6 minutes, stirring occasionally. Put the beans into a saucepan and heat gently, stirring occasionally.

2 Arrange the bacon rashers on the grill rack with the tomatoes. Cook for 4–5 minutes, turning the rashers once, until crispy.

3 Meanwhile, spray a large non-stick frying pan with the cooking spray. Carefully break in the eggs and cook over a medium heat for 2–3 minutes to set them.

4 Share the bacon, beans, mushrooms and tomatoes between 4 warm plates. While doing this, put the eggs under the grill for a few moments to set the surface. Serve seasoned with black pepper.

Variation Use turkey rashers instead of bacon – you can serve 3 rashers per person for the same *ProPoints* value of 6.

Following the Filling & Healthy day approach?
For this recipe use 2 of your weekly *ProPoints* allowance per serving.

ProPoints values to spare?

+1 by adding another 25 g (1 oz) lean back bacon rasher per portion.

+3 by serving each portion with 2 slices, 40 g (1½ oz) each of calorie controlled bread, toasted if you like, and each slice spread with 1 teaspoon of low fat spread.

COUNTRY COTTAGE *Pie*

A topping of mashed sweet potatoes, carrots and cauliflower gives this healthier version of cottage pie a new twist – and the portions are satisfyingly generous.

 ProPoints values per serving
ProPoints values per recipe 22

 Serves 4
Takes 35 minutes

300 g (10½ oz) sweet potatoes, cut into chunks
2 carrots, cut into chunks
1 cauliflower, broken into florets
400 g (14 oz) extra lean minced beef
1 onion, chopped finely
1 courgette, chopped finely
100 g (3½ oz) fine green beans, chopped
100 g (3½ oz) mushrooms, sliced
1 teaspoon dried mixed herbs
4 teaspoons gravy granules for beef
salt and freshly ground black pepper

1 Cook the sweet potatoes, carrots and cauliflower in a large saucepan of boiling water until tender – about 20 minutes.

2 Meanwhile, heat a large lidded saucepan and add the minced beef, a handful at a time, cooking over a high heat until seared and browned.

3 Add the onion, courgette, green beans, mushrooms and mixed herbs to the minced beef. Add 400 ml (14 fl oz) water and bring up to the boil. Simmer, partially covered, for 20 minutes.

4 Preheat the grill and warm a large baking dish under it for 1–2 minutes. Meanwhile, drain and mash the sweet potatoes, carrots and cauliflower, seasoning with black pepper.

5 Sprinkle the gravy granules into the mince mixture, stirring until thickened. Season if needed, then tip the mixture into the baking dish. Spoon the mash on top, spreading it out to cover the mince. Grill until lightly browned, then serve.

Cook's tip Searing and browning the meat is an important step that gives the dish a good flavour.

Following the Filling & Healthy day approach? You don't need to use any of your weekly *ProPoints* allowance for a serving of this recipe.

CHILLI
Con Carne

Adding lots of extra vegetables to your favourite dishes, like this chilli, increases their filling-power – it's a good habit to get into.

 ProPoints values per serving
ProPoints values per recipe 39

 Serves 4
Takes 40 minutes

400 g (14 oz) extra lean minced beef
1 large onion, chopped
2 garlic cloves, crushed
1 large carrot, chopped
1 red or yellow pepper, de-seeded and chopped
75 g (2¾ oz) fine green beans, chopped
1 courgette, coarsely grated
300 ml (10 fl oz) beef or vegetable stock
400 g can chopped tomatoes
410 g can mixed beans, rinsed and drained
2 tablespoons tomato purée
2–3 teaspoons medium or hot chilli powder
150 g (5½ oz) mushrooms, sliced
175 g (6 oz) dried long grain rice
salt and freshly ground black pepper
fresh coriander sprigs, to garnish (optional)

1 Heat a large heavy-based saucepan. Add the mince, a handful at a time. Sear it over a high heat, stirring after 30–40 seconds, then cooking for another 1–2 minutes until browned.

2 Add the onion, garlic, carrot, pepper, green beans and courgette. Cook, stirring, for a further 2–3 minutes.

3 Pour in the stock, tip in the tomatoes and mixed beans, then add the tomato purée, chilli powder and mushrooms. Stir well. Cover and simmer for 25–30 minutes.

4 About 15 minutes before serving, put the rice on to cook in plenty of boiling water – cook for 12 minutes, or according to the packet instructions, until tender. Drain well.

5 Check the chilli's seasoning, adding a little salt and pepper if needed. Serve with the rice and garnish with coriander, if using.

Cook's tip Take care when using chilli powder: add it to suit your taste and use a mild variety if you prefer.

Variation **V** For a vegetarian version, use a 500 g bag of frozen Quorn mince instead of beef – there's no need to sear it. The **ProPoints** values per serving will be 10.

Following the Filling & Healthy day approach?
For this recipe use 5 of your weekly **ProPoints** allowance per serving.

HOME-MADE
Turkey Burger

Turkey mince makes excellent burgers – and economical ones too. The family will soon gobble these up.

 7 *ProPoints* values per serving
ProPoints values per recipe 28

 Serves 4
Takes 20 minutes

450 g (1 lb) **turkey breast mince**
1 **onion**, chopped finely
1 **carrot**, grated
1 **courgette**, grated
2 teaspoons dried mixed herbs
1 tablespoon chopped **fresh parsley**
¼ teaspoon dried chilli flakes
   (optional)
calorie controlled cooking spray
4 standard burger buns
lettuce leaves, shredded
2 **tomatoes**, sliced
1 large **gherkin**, sliced
salt and freshly ground black pepper

1 Put the turkey mince in a large bowl and add the onion, carrot, courgette, mixed herbs, parsley and chilli flakes (if using). Season with salt and pepper, then form into 4 burgers. Cover and chill if cooking later, or freeze at this point.

2 Heat a char-grill pan or the grill. Spray the burgers with calorie controlled cooking spray, then cook for 4–5 minutes on each side, or until done to your liking.

3 Meanwhile, slice the burger buns in half and lightly toast the cut sides. Pile some lettuce on to the base of each bun. Place the cooked burgers on the bases, then arrange the tomato and gherkin slices on top, finishing with the bun lids. Serve at once.

Cook's tip Adding grated carrot and courgette bulks up the burgers and adds 'invisible' vegetables.

Variation For a traditional beef version, use **extra lean beef mince** instead of turkey – *ProPoints* values per serving will be 7.

Following the Filling & Healthy day approach?
For this recipe use 7 of your weekly *ProPoints* allowance per serving.

ProPoints values to spare?

+1 by serving each burger with 1 tablespoon of low fat mayonnaise.

+2 by topping each burger with 20 g (¾ oz) crumbled blue Stilton or a processed cheese slice.

+3 by topping each burger with 40 g (1½ oz) light halloumi cheese, grilled.

ULTIMATE RED THAI
Chicken Curry

Unlike Indian curries, Thai recipes are super-speedy.

 ProPoints values per serving
ProPoints values per recipe 41

 Serves 4
Takes 25 minutes

calorie controlled cooking spray
450 g (1 lb) skinless, boneless
   chicken breasts, cut into chunks
400 g can reduced fat coconut milk
300 ml (10 fl oz) chicken stock
2 tablespoons Thai red curry paste
2 tablespoons Thai fish sauce
2 teaspoons grated fresh root ginger
1 lemongrass stalk, bashed with a
   rolling pin
2 dried kaffir lime leaves
4 large banana shallots, sliced (or
   8 small shallots)
200 g (7 oz) long-stem broccoli,
   sliced
1 red pepper, de-seeded and
   chopped
100 g (3½ oz) mangetout or
   sugarsnap peas
1 red chilli (optional)
100 g (3½ oz) dried rice noodles
a small handful of fresh coriander
   leaves

1 Heat a wok or large frying pan and spray with the cooking spray. Add the chicken breast chunks and stir-fry for 2–3 minutes, until sealed and browned.

2 Tip in the coconut milk and stock, then stir in the Thai curry paste and fish sauce. Add the ginger, lemongrass, lime leaves and shallots. Heat to a gentle simmer and cook for 5–8 minutes.

3 Add the broccoli, pepper, mangetout or sugarsnap peas and chilli (if using). Simmer for 10 more minutes, then remove the lemongrass stalk. At the same time, soak the rice noodles in boiling water for 10 minutes.

4 Drain the noodles and add them to the curry, letting them heat through for a few moments. Ladle the curry into warmed bowls and serve with coriander sprinkled on top.

Cook's tip Take care that the liquid doesn't boil down too much – add a splash of water if necessary.

Variation Use Thai green curry paste instead of red, if you prefer.

Following the Filling & Healthy day approach?
For this recipe use 7 of your weekly *ProPoints* allowance per serving.

CHICKEN
Pasanda

Mild and fragrant, this lovely chicken curry is a real feast. If you're planning a Friday night dinner, start marinating the chicken on Thursday.

 ProPoints values per serving
ProPoints values per recipe 41

 Serves 4
Preparation time 15 minutes
　　+ minimum 2 hours marinating
Cooking time 30 minutes

4 tablespoons 0% fat Greek yogurt
1 teaspoon ground cumin
2 teaspoons ground coriander
3 cardamom pods, split
½ teaspoon ground turmeric
450 g (1 lb) skinless, boneless
　　chicken breasts, cut into chunks
calorie controlled cooking spray
1 large onion, chopped
2 garlic cloves, crushed
2 teaspoons grated fresh root ginger
200 ml (7 fl oz) chicken stock
2 tablespoons desiccated coconut
15 g (½ oz) sultanas
200 g (7 oz) dried basmati rice
15 g (½ oz) toasted flaked almonds
fresh coriander sprigs, to garnish
　　(optional)

1 Mix together the yogurt, cumin, coriander, cardamom pods and turmeric in a large non-metallic bowl with 2 tablespoons of water. Add the chicken, stir well, then cover and chill for at least 2 hours or, ideally, overnight.

2 When ready to cook, spray a large non-stick frying pan or wok with the cooking spray. Add the onion and cook gently for 5 minutes, then add the garlic and ginger and cook for another minute.

3 Tip in the chicken and yogurt mixture, then stir in the stock. Heat gently until almost boiling, then reduce the heat and add the coconut and sultanas. Simmer for 25 minutes, stirring frequently. After 15 minutes, put the rice on to cook in a saucepan of boiling water for 10–12 minutes, or according to the packet instructions.

4 Share the curry and rice between 4 warm serving plates. Serve sprinkled with the toasted almonds and garnished with coriander (if using).

Cook's tip Use 1 tablespoon of mild curry powder for the marinade instead of the cumin, coriander, cardamom and turmeric.

Variation Make the curry with the same amount of chunks of turkey breast instead. *ProPoints* values per serving will still be 10.

Following the Filling & Healthy day approach?
For this recipe use 7 of your weekly *ProPoints* allowance per serving.

CHICKEN CASSEROLE
with Sage and Onion Dumplings

Enjoy the wonderful aroma as this tasty chicken casserole simmers in the oven.

 ProPoints values per serving
ProPoints values per recipe 39

 Serves 4
Preparation time 25 minutes
Cooking time 1 hour 5 minutes

calorie controlled cooking spray
400 g (14 oz) skinless, boneless
    chicken thighs, cut into chunks
1 onion, chopped
400 g (14 oz) Chanteray carrots,
    halved lengthways
2 celery sticks, sliced
200 g (7 oz) swede, chopped
1 leek, sliced
850 ml (1½ pints) chicken stock
40 g (1½ oz) pearl barley, rinsed with
    boiling water
1 tablespoon chopped fresh parsley,
    plus extra, to serve
75 g (2¾ oz) frozen or canned
    sweetcorn
salt and freshly ground black pepper

For the dumplings
80 g (3 oz) self-raising flour
a pinch of salt
40 g (1½ oz) low fat spread
1 shallot, chopped very finely
2 teaspoons chopped fresh sage

1 Preheat the oven to Gas Mark 4/180°C/fan oven 160°C.

2 Heat a large heavy-based flameproof casserole dish on the hob and spray with the cooking spray. Add the chicken chunks and let them sear and brown for a few moments before turning them over. Stir, then cook them for another 2 minutes or so for them to brown. This helps to give the casserole a great flavour.

3 Add the onion, carrots, celery, swede and leek to the casserole dish. Pour in the stock and add the pearl barley and parsley. Season. Bring up to the boil, then cover and transfer to the oven to cook for 45 minutes.

4 To make the dumplings, put the flour and salt into a mixing bowl and rub in the low fat spread with your fingertips, until the mixture looks like crumbs. Add the shallot and sage, then stir in just enough cold water to make a soft (not sticky) dough. Shape the dough into 8 dumplings.

5 Stir the sweetcorn into the casserole, then arrange the dumplings on top. Cover and cook for a further 20 minutes. Check the seasoning, then serve the casserole sprinkled with chopped fresh parsley.

Cook's tip For the dumplings, you could use 2 tablespoons of finely chopped onion or spring onion instead of the shallot.

Variation Another time, make the casserole with turkey thigh meat instead of chicken. **ProPoints** values per serving will be 8.

Following the Filling & Healthy day approach?
For this recipe use 9 of your weekly **ProPoints** allowance per serving.

ROAST LOIN OF PORK
with a Rosemary and Thyme Crust

Pork loin is lean and succulent – and in this recipe a tasty crust replaces fatty crackling.
The leftover meat is delicious in sandwiches the next day.

 ProPoints values per serving **10**
ProPoints values per recipe 65

Serves 4
Preparation time 25 minutes
Cooking time 1¼ hours
   + 15 minutes resting

1 kg (2 lb 4 oz) pork loin joint,
   trimmed of skin and fat
4 tablespoons fresh breadcrumbs
finely grated zest of 1 lemon
1 shallot, chopped very finely
1 tablespoon chopped fresh
   rosemary
1 tablespoon chopped fresh thyme
1 small egg, beaten
2 teaspoons vegetable oil
700 g (1 lb 9 oz) Charlotte or new
   potatoes, cut into chunks
400 g (14 oz) carrots, sliced
400 g (14 oz) swede, cut into cubes
400 g (14 oz) butternut squash, cut
   into cubes
4 teaspoons chicken gravy granules
salt and freshly ground black pepper

1 Preheat the oven to Gas Mark 6/200°C/fan oven 180°C.

2 Put the pork in a roasting tin. Mix together the breadcrumbs, lemon zest, shallot, rosemary, thyme and egg. Season with salt and pepper, then press the mixture over the top of the pork. Transfer to the oven and roast for 30 minutes.

3 Take the pork out of the oven and cover with a piece of foil. Put the vegetable oil into a separate roasting tin and add all the vegetables, tossing to coat. Return the pork to the oven and roast the vegetables above it for 40–45 minutes, turning them after 25 minutes.

4 Cover the pork with a fresh piece of foil and let it rest for 10–15 minutes before carving. The vegetables can stay in the switched-off oven to keep hot.

5 Make the gravy according to the packet instructions. Carve half the pork joint into 8 slices, serving 2 slices per person, with an equal amount of roast vegetables and gravy.

Following the Filling & Healthy day approach?
For this recipe use 2 of your weekly **ProPoints** allowance per serving.

LAMB AND APRICOT
Tagine

Enjoy the blend of flavours in this slow-cooked Moroccan lamb dish.

 9 *ProPoints* values per serving
ProPoints values per recipe 35

 Serves 4
Preparation time 15 minutes
Cooking time 1 hour

calorie controlled cooking spray
350 g (12 oz) lean lamb chunks (such
   as leg or rump)
1 tablespoon harissa paste
2 teaspoons ras-el-hanout seasoning
2 red onions, chopped
2 carrots, sliced
1 red pepper, de-seeded and cut
   into chunks
600 ml (20 fl oz) lamb or vegetable
   stock
2 tablespoons tomato purée
411 g can apricot halves in natural
   juice, drained
125 g (4½ oz) giant couscous
1 tablespoon cornflour
4 tablespoons low fat natural yogurt
1 tablespoon chopped fresh mint,
   plus mint sprigs, to garnish

1 Heat a large lidded saucepan and spray with the cooking spray. Add the lamb chunks, letting them sear and brown before turning them over. Cook for 3–4 minutes until browned on all sides.

2 Add the harissa paste, ras-el-hanout seasoning, onions, carrots, pepper, stock and tomato purée. Bring up to the boil, then reduce the heat. Cover and simmer for 40 minutes, adding extra water, if needed.

3 Add the apricots to the pan and simmer for 15 minutes more. At the same time, put the couscous into a saucepan and cover with cold water. Bring up to the boil, then reduce the heat and simmer for 10–12 minutes until swollen and tender.

4 Blend the cornflour with 2 tablespoons of cold water, then add it to the lamb mixture, stirring until thickened. Cook for 1–2 minutes.

5 Mix the yogurt with the mint. Serve the lamb tagine with the couscous, topping each portion with 1 tablespoon of the yogurt mixture, and garnishing with extra mint.

Following the Filling & Healthy day approach?
For this recipe use 8 of your weekly *ProPoints* allowance per serving.

ProPoints values to spare?

+2 by sprinkling 15 g toasted flaked almonds over each portion before serving.

CLASSIC
Fish Pie

A favourite fish pie has to feature on your menu. It's a great dish for a family gathering, as you can prepare it ahead so that it's ready to go in the oven when everyone arrives.

ProPoints values per serving
ProPoints values per recipe 38

Serves 4
Preparation time 20 minutes
Cooking time 40 minutes

500 g (1 lb 2 oz) potatoes, peeled and cut into large chunks
500 g (1 lb 2 oz) butternut squash, peeled, de-seeded and cut into large chunks
15 g (½ oz) low fat spread
40 g (1½ oz) plain flour
400 ml (14 fl oz) skimmed milk, plus 2 tablespoons
2 tablespoons chopped fresh parsley
50 g (1¾ oz) frozen peas
200 g (7 oz) skinless smoked haddock, cut into chunks
100 g (3½ oz) skinless salmon fillet, cut into chunks
200 g (7 oz) skinless coley, cod or haddock, cut into chunks
150 g (5½ oz) cooked, peeled prawns, thawed if frozen
salt and freshly ground black pepper

1 Cook the potatoes and butternut squash in boiling water for 20 minutes, until tender.

2 Meanwhile, make the sauce. Put the low fat spread, flour and milk (reserving the 2 tablespoons) into a large non-stick saucepan. Heat, stirring constantly with a small whisk until thickened and smooth. Remove from the heat and add the parsley and peas. Season to taste. Preheat the oven to Gas Mark 5/190°C/fan oven 170°C.

3 Mix the chunks of fish and prawns together and put them into a large baking dish. Pour the sauce on top and mix it in a little.

4 Drain and mash the potatoes and butternut squash, then beat in the reserved milk and season with black pepper. Spoon on top of the fish mixture and spread it out evenly. Bake for 30–35 minutes. If you like, grill the surface for 3–4 minutes so that it's really brown when you serve the pie.

Cook's tips You can buy pre-packed mixed fish chunks, which can work out cheaper than buying the fish separately. Look out for them in the chiller cabinet, or buy them from the fish counter.

The all-in-one method in step 2 is the best way to make a smooth, lump-free white sauce.

Variation Use a mixture of 300 g (10½ oz) smoked haddock and 300 g (10½ oz) white fish instead and add some lightly cooked broccoli florets to the sauce. ***ProPoints*** values will be 9 per serving.

Following the Filling & Healthy day approach?
For this recipe use 1 of your weekly ***ProPoints*** allowance per serving.

PERFECT PRAWN
Biriyani

Ideal for a supper in front of the TV – this is fork food at its best.

 ProPoints values per serving
ProPoints values per recipe 20

 Serves 2
Takes 20 minutes

150 g (5½ oz) dried long grain rice
calorie controlled cooking spray
4 spring onions, chopped finely
1 garlic clove, crushed
1 small red pepper, de-seeded and
    chopped
75 g (2¾ oz) fine green beans,
    chopped
2 teaspoons medium curry powder
½ teaspoon cumin seeds
200 g (7 oz) frozen cooked peeled
    prawns
50 g (1¾ oz) frozen peas
freshly ground black pepper

1 Cook the rice in a saucepan of boiling water for 10–12 minutes, or according to the packet instructions, until tender.

2 Meanwhile, spray a large non-stick frying pan or wok with the cooking spray and gently fry the spring onions, garlic, pepper and green beans for 3–4 minutes, until softened.

3 Add the curry powder and cumin seeds and stir for another minute, then add the frozen prawns and peas and cook for 2–3 minutes, stirring often.

4 Drain the rice thoroughly and add it to the frying pan or wok. Season with black pepper and stir the ingredients together. Pile on to warm serving plates and serve at once.

Cook's tip Keep spices and rice in your kitchen cupboard and prawns and peas in your freezer, then you can create this recipe at a moment's notice.

Variations Use a large onion instead of spring onions; a yellow or orange pepper instead of a red one, and a courgette or runner beans instead of fine beans.

Following the Filling & Healthy day approach?
For this recipe use 7 of your weekly **ProPoints** allowance per serving.

ROASTED VEGETABLE
Lasagne

This vegetarian lasagne is another one of my favourites – perfect for all the family.

 8 *ProPoints* values per serving
ProPoints values per recipe 30

 Serves 4
Preparation time 40 minutes
 Cooking time 35 minutes

500 g (1 lb 2 oz) butternut squash,
   peeled, de-seeded and cut into
   2 cm (¾ inch) chunks
1 red onion, cut into wedges
1 yellow or orange pepper,
   de-seeded and cut into chunks
1 large courgette, cut into chunks
1 tablespoon olive oil
12 cherry tomatoes, halved
500 g carton or jar of passata
6 dried lasagne sheets, weighing
   about 100 g (3½ oz)
salt and freshly ground black pepper

For the sauce
15 g (½ oz) low fat spread
25 g (1 oz) plain flour
300 ml (10 fl oz) skimmed milk
50 g (1¾ oz) half fat Cheddar cheese,
   grated

1 Preheat the oven to Gas Mark 6/200°C/fan oven 180°C.

2 Put the butternut squash, red onion, pepper and courgette into a large roasting tin and add the olive oil. Season and toss to coat. Roast for 20–30 minutes, until the vegetables are tender.

3 Add the cherry tomatoes to the roasted vegetables, then stir in the passata.

4 Tip half the vegetable mixture into a large rectangular baking dish, measuring about 25 x 20 cm (10 x 8 inches). Arrange 3 lasagne sheets on top. Repeat the layers.

5 Make the cheese sauce. Put the low fat spread, flour and milk into a non-stick saucepan. Heat, stirring constantly with a small whisk until thickened and smooth (see Cook's tip, page 68). Pour evenly over the top of the lasagne and sprinkle with the grated cheese. Bake for 30–35 minutes, until cooked and golden brown. Allow to stand for a few minutes, then serve.

Variation Stir 150 g (5½ oz) sliced mushrooms into the roasted vegetables when you add the passata. *ProPoints* values will stay the same.

Following the Filling & Healthy day approach?
For this recipe use 7 of your weekly *ProPoints* allowance per serving.

ProPoints values to spare?

+2 per portion for non-vegetarians by roasting 100 g (3½ oz) sliced chorizo sausage with the vegetables for the final 10 minutes at step 2.

POTATO AND AUBERGINE
Moussaka

A clever mix of lamb mince and Quorn keeps the *ProPoints* values lower than usual in this delicious moussaka.

 10 *ProPoints* values per serving
ProPoints values per recipe 39

 Serves 4
Preparation time 25 minutes
Cooking time 45 minutes

450 g (1 lb) potatoes, sliced
200 g (7 oz) lean lamb mince
300 g bag frozen Quorn mince
1 large onion, chopped
2 garlic cloves, crushed
1 courgette, grated
100 ml (3½ fl oz) vegetable stock
400 g can chopped tomatoes
2 teaspoons dried oregano
2 tablespoons tomato purée
1 large aubergine, sliced
salt and freshly ground black pepper

For the topping
150 g (5½ oz) 0% fat Greek yogurt
1 egg
2 tablespoons skimmed milk
75 g (2¾ oz) half fat Cheddar cheese, finely grated

1 Preheat the oven to Gas Mark 5/190°C/fan oven 170°C.

2 Par-cook the sliced potatoes in simmering water for 5–6 minutes. Drain well.

3 At the same time, heat a large non-stick saucepan and add the lamb mince, searing it over a high heat for 3–4 minutes, until browned. Add the frozen Quorn mince, onion, garlic, courgette, stock, tomatoes, oregano and tomato purée. Stir well and simmer for 5 minutes. Season.

4 Tip half the mince mixture into a large rectangular baking dish and arrange the aubergine slices on top. Spoon the rest of the mince mixture over them, then finish with a layer of potatoes.

5 Make the topping by beating the yogurt, egg and milk together. Spread it evenly over the potatoes, then sprinkle the cheese on top. Bake for 40–45 minutes, until golden brown.

Cook's tip Make one moussaka and freeze one by doubling up the quantities.

Variation **V** For a vegetarian version, omit the lamb and use a 500 g bag of frozen Quorn mince. This will reduce the *ProPoints* values to 8 per serving.

Following the Filling & Healthy day approach?
For this recipe use 5 of your weekly *ProPoints* allowance per serving.

MACARONI
Cauliflower Cheese

By combining cauliflower cheese with macaroni cheese – and trimming down some ingredients – you'll be able to keep the *ProPoints* values in check.

 ProPoints values per serving
ProPoints values per recipe 38

 Serves 4
Takes 20 minutes

250 g (9 oz) dried macaroni
1 cauliflower, broken into florets
15 g (½ oz) low fat spread
40 g (1½ oz) plain flour
450 ml (16 fl oz) skimmed milk
1 teaspoon wholegrain mustard
12 cherry tomatoes, halved
50 g (1¾ oz) half fat Cheddar cheese, grated
salt and freshly ground black pepper

1 Cook the macaroni in a large saucepan of boiling water for 5 minutes, then add the cauliflower. Cook for a further 5–6 minutes, until the pasta and cauliflower are tender.

2 Meanwhile, put the low fat spread, flour and milk into a non-stick saucepan. Heat, stirring constantly with a small whisk until thickened and smooth (see Cook's tip, page 68). Remove from the heat and add the mustard. Season to taste.

3 Preheat the grill to medium hot. Warm a large grill-proof baking dish underneath it.

4 Drain the cooked pasta and cauliflower thoroughly – if they are too wet they will make the sauce runny. Tip them into the baking dish and pour the hot sauce on top. Dot the cherry tomatoes over the surface and sprinkle with the grated cheese. Grill for 5–6 minutes until browned and piping hot, then serve.

Variation You could use half cauliflower and half broccoli florets.

Following the Filling & Healthy day approach?
For this recipe use 8 of your weekly *ProPoints* allowance per serving.

ProPoints values to spare?

+1 per portion by adding an extra 50 g (1¾ oz) half fat Cheddar cheese to the recipe, grating it into the hot sauce.

VEGGIE
Spag Bol

You must try this vegetarian version of spaghetti Bolognese – it's tasty and economical. Adding extra veg keeps *ProPoints* values low, yet there's no compromise on flavour.

 8 *ProPoints* values per serving
ProPoints values per recipe 33

 Serves 4
Preparation time 20 minutes
 Cooking time 30 minutes

500 g bag frozen Quorn mince
1 large onion, chopped
2 garlic cloves, crushed
2 celery sticks, chopped
1 large carrot, chopped
1 courgette, chopped
400 ml (14 fl oz) vegetable stock
400 g can chopped tomatoes
2 teaspoons Italian mixed dried herbs
2 tablespoons tomato purée
200 g (7 oz) mushrooms, sliced
200 g (7 oz) dried spaghetti
salt and freshly ground black pepper
fresh basil leaves, to garnish

1 Heat a large heavy-based, lidded saucepan. Tip in the frozen Quorn mince and add the onion, garlic, celery, carrot, courgette and stock. Bring up to the boil.

2 Add the tomatoes and the dried herbs, tomato purée and mushrooms. Stir well. Simmer, partially covered, for 25–30 minutes. Check the seasoning, adding a little salt and pepper, if needed.

3 After 15 minutes, cook the spaghetti in plenty of boiling water for 10–12 minutes, or according to the packet instructions. Drain well, share between 4 warm plates and top with the sauce. Serve garnished with basil leaves.

Cook's tip You can make a traditional meat version with 500 g (1 lb 2 oz) extra lean beef mince, dry-frying it in the saucepan until browned, before adding the rest of the ingredients. *ProPoints* values per portion will be 9.

Variation Halving the quantity of spaghetti and cooking pared strips of carrot and courgette with the rest of the pasta will reduce the *ProPoints* values to 6 per serving.

Following the Filling & Healthy day approach?
For this recipe use 5 of your weekly *ProPoints* allowance per serving.

"I ALWAYS SWAP CREAM FOR *low fat crème fraîche to lower the ProPoints* VALUES BUT KEEP THE CREAMY CONSISTENCY. *I also grate veg into chilli,* LASAGNE ETC. TO BULK IT OUT FOR ZERO PROPOINTS VALUES."

Rachel Smith Weight Watchers member

POINT Stretchers

PROPOINTS VALUES

SWEET CHILLI DUCK
with Sesame Noodles

The way to stretch your *ProPoints* allowance is to make a little go a long way, padding out meals with lots of fresh vegetables to add colour, vibrancy and vitamins.

 ProPoints values per serving
ProPoints values per recipe 31

Serves 4
Takes 15 minutes

175 g (6 oz) wholewheat noodles
1 teaspoon toasted sesame oil
2 x 150 g (5½ oz) skinless duck breasts approx. 300 g (10½ oz) total weight, sliced thinly
1 tablespoon sweet chilli sauce
1 large carrot, cut into matchstick strips
1 red pepper, de-seeded and sliced thinly
1 yellow pepper, de-seeded and sliced thinly
150 g (5½ oz) sugarsnap peas or mangetout, halved
200 g (7 oz) baby corn, halved
1 teaspoon Chinese five spice powder
2 teaspoons sesame seeds, toasted

1 Cover the noodles with boiling water and soak for 6 minutes, or prepare them according to the packet instructions.

2 At the same time, heat the sesame oil in a wok or large frying pan and add the sliced duck breasts, stir-frying over a high heat for 3–4 minutes until cooked. Tip them into a bowl and add the chilli sauce, tossing to coat. Cover and keep warm.

3 Add all the vegetables to the wok or frying pan and stir-fry over a high heat for 4–5 minutes until cooked, yet still crunchy. Stir in the Chinese five spice powder.

4 Drain the noodles thoroughly and add them to the wok, stirring them through gently, and reheating for about 1 minute. Share between 4 warm plates or bowls, dividing the duck and chilli sauce between them. Serve sprinkled with the sesame seeds.

Cook's tip Take care that you don't overcook the duck or it will become dry.

Variation Make this recipe with 2 x 165 g (5¾ oz) skinless, boneless chicken breasts instead of duck. *ProPoints* values per serving will be 7.

Following the Filling & Healthy day approach?
For this recipe use 8 of your weekly *ProPoints* allowance per serving.

ProPoints values to spare?

+1 by serving each portion with 1 tablespoon of sweet chilli sauce.

CUMIN-SPICED CAULIFLOWER
and Squash

Enjoy this recipe as a tasty filler when you don't have many *ProPoints* values to spare.

ProPoints values per serving 1
ProPoints values per recipe 4

Serves 4
Takes 35 minutes

500 g (1 lb 2 oz) butternut squash, peeled, de-seeded and cut into chunks
calorie controlled cooking spray
1 medium cauliflower, broken into florets
2 teaspoons olive oil
1 small red onion, sliced thinly
1 teaspoon cumin seeds
2 tablespoons fresh breadcrumbs
finely grated zest of 1 lemon
salt and freshly ground black pepper

1 Preheat the oven to Gas Mark 6/200°C/fan oven 180°C.

2 Arrange the butternut squash chunks in a large roasting tin and spray with the cooking spray. Bake in the oven for 25–30 minutes, or until tender, turning once.

3 About 10 minutes before the butternut squash is ready, cook the cauliflower in simmering water until just tender (don't allow it to get too soft). Drain well.

4 Heat the olive oil in a large non-stick frying pan and cook the red onion until softened – about 4–5 minutes. Add the cumin seeds, breadcrumbs and lemon zest and cook until the breadcrumbs are browned. Add the drained cauliflower, tossing gently to coat, season and cooking for another 2–3 minutes. Tip into the roasting tin and stir gently into the butternut squash. Serve immediately.

Cook's tip It's best if the cauliflower is slightly underdone to retain a little 'bite', otherwise it will become mushy when mixed with the other ingredients.

Following the Filling & Healthy day approach?
For this recipe use 1 of your weekly *ProPoints* allowance per serving.

ProPoints values to spare?

+1 by sprinkling each portion with 1 tablespoon of ready-made croûtons.

+1 by topping each portion with 1 tablespoon of half fat crème fraîche.

+1 by chopping 20 g (¾ oz) roasted cashew nuts and sprinkling an equal amount over each portion.

HAM AND ASPARAGUS ROLLS

This great idea is just the thing for a tasty packed lunch or after-work snack.

 ProPoints values per serving
ProPoints values per recipe 10

Serves 2
Takes 10 minutes

6 chunky **asparagus** spears
100 g (3½ oz) low fat soft cheese
1 teaspoon wholegrain mustard
1 teaspoon finely chopped **fresh
    chives** or **spring onion**
6 x 30 g (1¼ oz) thin slices **lean roast
    ham**
freshly ground black pepper

1 Cook the asparagus spears in simmering water for 4–5 minutes. Rinse with cold water, then drain well.

2 Meanwhile, mix together the soft cheese, mustard and chives or spring onion. Lay the slices of ham on a work surface. Spread an equal amount of the cheese mixture along one side of each piece of ham, then place a cold asparagus spear on top. Season with black pepper and roll up tightly.

3 Eat immediately, or wrap 3 ham rolls in cling film for each serving and keep cool until ready to serve.

Cook's tip Make sure you choose thin slices of ham, as thick ones won't roll up.

Following the Filling & Healthy day approach?
For this recipe use 2 of your weekly **ProPoints** allowance per serving.

TWO-POTATO SALAD

This interesting salad uses a combination of ordinary and sweet potatoes.

 ProPoints values per serving
ProPoints values per recipe 10

 Serves 2
Takes 10 minutes + cooling

200 g (7oz) Charlotte or new
    potatoes, scrubbed and cut into
    small chunks
150 g (5½ oz) **sweet potatoes**,
    peeled and cut into small chunks
2 tablespoons **low fat plain yogurt**
25 g (1 oz) low fat soft cheese
2 **spring onions**, chopped finely
salt and freshly ground black pepper

1 Cook the potatoes and sweet potatoes in boiling water for 5–8 minutes, until just tender. Drain, rinse with cold water and leave to cool.

2 Mix together the yogurt and soft cheese, then stir in the spring onions. Add the cooled potatoes, season, and mix together gently. Keep cool until ready to serve.

Variation You could make the salad with 350 g (12 oz) of ordinary potatoes, without using any sweet potato. **ProPoints** values per portion would be the same.

Following the Filling & Healthy day approach? You don't need to use any of your weekly **ProPoints** allowance for a serving of this recipe.

GRILLED FISH
with Tomatoes, Lemon and Chives

Grilled white fish is a great choice for a low *ProPoints* value meal. Serve it with carrot, swede and potato mash to stretch your *ProPoints* allowance even further.

 ProPoints values per serving
ProPoints values per recipe 20

Serves 4
Takes 25 minutes

500 g (1 lb 2 oz) **potatoes**, cut into chunks
500 g (1 lb 2 oz) **carrots**, sliced
1 **swede**, cut into chunks
4 x 125 g (4½ oz) **haddock** or **cod** fillets
finely grated zest and juice of 1 lemon
2 **tomatoes**, sliced
salt and freshly ground black pepper
chopped **fresh chives**, to garnish

1 Cook the potatoes, carrots and swede in a large saucepan of boiling water for about 20 minutes, until tender.

2 When the vegetables have been cooking for 10 minutes, preheat the grill. Arrange the fish fillets on the grill rack and sprinkle them with the lemon zest and juice. Season with black pepper. Cook for 3–4 minutes, then arrange the sliced tomatoes on top and grill for another 3–4 minutes, depending on the thickness of the fillets.

3 Drain the vegetables, then mash them thoroughly. Season to taste, share between 4 plates and serve with the fish, sprinkling the chives on top and seasoning with black pepper.

Cook's tip Take care not to overcook the fish, or it will become dry. The flesh should be opaque and should flake easily when tested with a fork. If it's ready before the mash, just turn off the grill, cover the fish with foil and let it rest for a few minutes.

Variation Choose any firm white fish for this recipe, such as **huss**, **whiting** or **coley**.

Following the Filling & Healthy day approach? You don't need to use any of your weekly *ProPoints* allowance for a serving of this recipe.

ProPoints values to spare?

+1 per portion by grilling 2 medium rashers (40 g/1½ oz) of streaky bacon alongside the fish until it's really crispy and crumbling it over the fish fillets.

+1 by topping each portion with 2 teaspoons of finely grated Parmesan cheese, sprinkling it over the tomatoes and grilling for the final 2 minutes.

CHICKEN, LEEK
and Barley Broth

Filling and satisfying, this soup makes one chicken breast go a long way.

 ProPoints values per serving
ProPoints values per recipe 13

 Serves 4
Takes 45 minutes

1.5 litres (2¾ pints) chicken or
    vegetable stock
1 large **onion**, chopped
1 large **carrot**, diced
1 **leek**, sliced
2 **celery** sticks, sliced thinly
1 teaspoon dried mixed herbs
75 g (3 oz) pearl barley
165 g (5¾ oz) **skinless, boneless
chicken breast**
1 tablespoon chopped **fresh parsley**
salt and freshly ground black pepper

1 Put the stock into a large lidded saucepan with the onion, carrot, leek, celery, dried herbs and pearl barley. Bring up to the boil, stirring occasionally.

2 Add the whole chicken breast, then reduce the heat and simmer, partially covered, for 30–35 minutes, until the vegetables are tender and the barley is plump and soft.

3 Lift out the chicken breast and shred it with two forks. Return it to the soup, then add the parsley. Season to taste and serve.

Cook's tip Cool any leftover soup as quickly as possible, then store in the fridge in a covered container for up to 2 days. Reheat thoroughly.

Variation Use a bunch of **spring onions** instead of the large onion, and try dried oregano or mixed Italian herbs instead of regular ones.

Following the Filling & Healthy day approach?
For this recipe use 2 of your weekly **ProPoints** allowance per serving.

ProPoints values to spare?

+1 by serving each portion with a 20 g (¾ oz) slice of calorie controlled bread, toasted.

+1 by serving each portion with 1 tablespoon of ready-made croûtons.

CARROT, CUMIN
and Red Lentil Dip

Prep this in advance and you've got a low *ProPoints* value snack for those needy times – perfect for dipping into when you arrive home from work starving.

 3 *ProPoints* values per serving
ProPoints values per recipe 16

 Serves 6
Takes 50 minutes + cooling

500 g (1 lb 2 oz) carrots, sliced
1 onion, chopped
2 garlic cloves, crushed
100 g (3½ oz) dried red lentils
500 ml (18 fl oz) vegetable stock
200 g (7 oz) low fat soft cheese with
    garlic and herbs
1 teaspoon ground cumin
1 teaspoon mild paprika
salt and freshly ground black pepper
raw vegetables, cut into sticks
    (cucumber, peppers, cauliflower,
    celery, etc.)

1 Cook the carrots, onion, garlic and red lentils in the vegetable stock for about 45 minutes, until the liquid has almost evaporated. Drain thoroughly and set aside to cool in a colander or large sieve.

2 Blend the carrot mixture until smooth, then add the soft cheese, cumin and paprika, and blend together. Season.

3 Tip the mixture into a bowl and serve with the raw vegetables. It will keep, covered, in the fridge for up to 5 days.

Cook's tips If you don't already have one, a hand-held stick blender is really useful and not expensive. It will come in handy for blending soups, sauces – and this dip.

Or go low-tech and use a potato masher to mash the carrots and lentils, and a wooden spoon for beating everything together.

Variation You could use a 410 g can of drained cannellini beans in water instead of the red lentils, adding them to the cooked carrots. Reduce the vegetable stock to 425 ml (15 fl oz) for 2 *ProPoints* values per serving.

Following the Filling & Healthy day approach?
For this recipe use 1 of your weekly *ProPoints* allowance per serving.

ProPoints values to spare?

+1 per portion by adding 35 g (1¼ oz) of finely chopped plain peanuts to the dip.

+1 by serving each portion with a 20 g (¾ oz) slice of calorie controlled bread, toasted.

ASIAN PRAWN NOODLE *Salad*

This salad is mainly an assembly job – so although there are quite a few ingredients, it's quick to put together.

 ProPoints values per serving
ProPoints values per recipe 18

Serves 4
Takes 20 minutes

300 g (10½ oz) large cooked peeled prawns
1 tablespoon soy sauce
1 tablespoon sweet chilli sauce
finely grated zest and juice of 1 lime
2 teaspoons finely grated fresh root ginger
1 shallot or 3 spring onions, sliced finely
300 g packet ready-cooked fine rice noodles
1 red and 1 yellow pepper, de-seeded and cut into fine strips
1 head pak choi, roughly shredded
½ head Chinese leaf lettuce, shredded
2 teaspoons sesame seeds
freshly ground black pepper

1 Put the prawns into a large salad bowl and add the soy sauce, sweet chilli sauce, lime zest and juice, ginger and shallot or spring onions. Toss to coat.

2 Put the noodles into a heatproof bowl and pour over enough boiling water to cover them. Leave for 2 minutes.

3 Meanwhile, add the peppers, pak choi and Chinese leaf lettuce to the salad bowl. Add the sesame seeds, then season with black pepper.

4 Drain the noodles thoroughly in a colander. Add them to the salad bowl and toss gently to mix together.

Cook's tip Toasting the sesame seeds in a dry frying pan until lightly browned will give them a lovely flavour.

Variation Use a shredded Little Gem lettuce instead of Chinese leaf lettuce, if you prefer.

Following the Filling & Healthy day approach?
For this recipe use 3 of your weekly **ProPoints** allowance per serving.

ASPARAGUS, COURGETTE
and Plum Tomato Pasta

Use this clever trick of cooking fine courgette strips with the pasta to make it go further.

 6 *ProPoints* values per serving
ProPoints values per recipe 25

Serves 4
Takes 20 minutes

450 g (1 lb) fine asparagus spears
calorie controlled cooking spray
200 g (7 oz) dried tagliatelle
2 courgettes, pared into ribbons (use a potato peeler)
16 baby plum or cherry tomatoes, halved
2 tablespoons green pesto
salt and freshly ground black pepper
4 teaspoons finely grated Parmesan cheese, to serve
fresh basil leaves, to serve

1 Preheat a char-grill pan or the grill. Spray the asparagus with the cooking spray and char-grill or grill, in batches, until tender.

2 At the same time, cook the tagliatelle in a large saucepan of boiling water for 10–12 minutes, or according to the packet instructions, until tender, adding the courgette strips for the final 3–4 minutes of cooking time.

3 Drain the cooked tagliatelle and courgettes, reserving 2–3 tablespoons of the cooking water, returning them and the reserved liquid to the saucepan.

4 Slice the asparagus spears into 3–4 pieces and add them to the saucepan with the tomatoes and pesto sauce. Stir everything together gently, reheating for 1–2 minutes. Season, then share between 4 warm serving bowls or plates, sprinkling each portion with 1 teaspoon of Parmesan cheese and a few basil leaves.

Cook's tip Fresh basil leaves add lots of flavour, meaning you don't need to stir in as much pesto sauce. When you buy a basil plant from the supermarket or greengrocer, take it out of its packaging and stand the pot in a shallow bowl, watering it from below. Put it on a sunny windowsill and water regularly, picking off any tired leaves, and it will keep growing for weeks.

Following the Filling & Healthy day approach?
For this recipe use 6 of your weekly *ProPoints* allowance per serving.

GRIDDLED COURGETTES
with Feta and Peas

Excellent as a starter, perfect as an accompaniment to a main meal, or just pile the courgettes on to a plateful of salad leaves for a lovely light lunch.

ProPoints values per serving
ProPoints values per recipe 6

 Serves 4
Takes 20 minutes

2 large courgettes, trimmed
100 g (3½ oz) frozen petits pois or garden peas
1 tablespoon lemon juice
2 teaspoons olive oil
½ teaspoon Dijon mustard
2 teaspoons balsamic vinegar
50 g (1¾ oz) light feta cheese, crumbled
freshly ground black pepper

1 Preheat a char-grill pan or the grill. Cut the courgettes in half horizontally, then slice each half lengthways into thin strips. Char-grill or grill on both sides, in batches, until tender.

2 Cook the peas in boiling water for 2–3 minutes. Drain well. Share the courgettes and peas between 4 plates.

3 Mix together the lemon juice, olive oil, mustard and balsamic vinegar. Sprinkle over the courgettes and top with the feta cheese. Serve seasoned with black pepper.

Cook's tip You don't need to spray the courgette slices with calorie controlled cooking spray, as they should cook in the hot char-grill pan (or under the grill) without oil. Char-grilling will give the best flavour.

Variation You could add char-grilled aubergine slices and peppers if you like, without adding any further **ProPoints** values.

Following the Filling & Healthy day approach?
For this recipe use 1 of your weekly **ProPoints** allowance per serving.

ProPoints values to spare?

+1 by serving 3 Melba toasts with each portion.

+1 per portion by sprinkling the salad with 3 tablespoons of toasted sunflower seeds before serving. Toast them lightly first to bring out their flavour.

CRISPBREAD TOPPERS

When you fancy a quick snack or light lunch, crispbreads are a good choice.

Lemon Curd and Banana

5 *ProPoints* values per serving
ProPoints values per recipe 10

 Serves 2

Take 4 fruit crunch crispbreads and spread each one with 2 teaspoons of low fat soft cheese, then spread 1 teaspoon of lemon curd on top of each one to give a lovely lemon cheesecake flavour. Slice 1 large **banana** and share it between the crispbreads and serve 2 per person.

Following the Filling & Healthy day approach?
For this recipe use 5 of your weekly *ProPoints* allowance per serving.

Tuna and Cucumber

4 *ProPoints* values per serving
ProPoints values per recipe 9

Serves 2

Drain a 160 g can of **tuna in water**, and mix it with 1 tablespoon **0% fat Greek yogurt**, 1 tablespoon reduced fat mayonnaise and 1 tablespoon finely chopped **cucumber**. Spread over 4 rye crispbreads and serve 2 per person, topped with thinly sliced **red onion** or **spring onion**.

Cottage Cheese and Marmite

3 *ProPoints* values per serving
ProPoints values per recipe 6

 Serves 2

Spread a little Marmite thinly over 4 sesame seed crispbreads, then top each one with 25 g (1 oz) **low fat cottage cheese**. Arrange some thin slices of **cucumber** on top, then serve 2 per person, garnished with **fresh mint** leaves.

Curried Chicken and Mango

5 *ProPoints* values per serving
ProPoints values per recipe 10

Serves 2

Mix 1 teaspoon of medium curry paste with 2 tablespoons of **low fat natural yogurt**. Slice a roasted 165 g (5¾ oz) **skinless, boneless chicken breast** and toss it in the curried yogurt, then share between 4 multi-grain crispbreads. Peel, stone and slice 1 small **mango**, arrange the slices on the crispbreads. Serve 2 per person, garnished with thinly sliced red chilli, if liked.

Following the Filling & Healthy day approach? For each of the above recipes use 2 of your weekly *ProPoints* allowance per serving.

BAKED POTATO FILLERS

Here's some inspiration for your lunchtime baked potato.

Feta with Cucumber and Tomato Salsa

 5 *ProPoints* values per serving
ProPoints values per recipe 11

 Serves 2

Bake 2 x 200 g (7 oz) **potatoes** at Gas Mark 6/200°C/fan oven 180°C for about 1 hour, until tender. For the filling, mix together 2 chopped **tomatoes**, ¼ chopped **cucumber**, 4 chopped **spring onions** and 1 tablespoon of chopped **fresh coriander**. Stir in 50 g (1¾ oz) of reduced fat feta cheese, cut into small chunks, and share between the potatoes.

Following the Filling & Healthy day approach? For this recipe use 1 of your weekly *ProPoints* allowance per serving.

Curried Chicken

 9 *ProPoints* values per serving
ProPoints values per recipe 18

Serves 2

Bake 2 x 200 g (7 oz) **potatoes** at Gas Mark 6/200°C/fan oven 180°C for about 1 hour, until tender. For the filling, mix 1 teaspoon of medium curry powder with 2 tablespoons of **low fat natural yogurt** and 1 tablespoon of reduced fat mayonnaise. Slice a roasted 165 g (5¾ oz) **skinless**, **boneless chicken breast** and add it to the curry mixture with 1 tablespoon of sultanas. Share between the potatoes and serve, sprinkled with chopped **fresh coriander**, **chives** or **parsley** and a few dried chilli flakes, if liked.

Following the Filling & Healthy day approach? For this recipe use 2 of your weekly *ProPoints* allowance per serving.

Spicy Beans and Pepper

 9 *ProPoints* values per serving
ProPoints values per recipe 18

 Serves 2

Bake 2 x 200 g (7 oz) **potatoes** at Gas Mark 6/200°C/fan oven 180°C for about 1 hour, until tender. For the filling, heat a 420 g can of reduced sugar and salt **baked beans** with 1 small red **pepper** (de-seeded and chopped) and 3 finely chopped **spring onions**. Add a de-seeded and finely chopped fresh green **chilli** or a pinch of dried red chilli flakes, if you like, then share between the baked potatoes.

Following the Filling & Healthy day approach? You don't need to use any of your weekly *ProPoints* allowance for a serving of this recipe.

COUSCOUS
and Quinoa Salad

Grains are great for filling you up, so make them a regular part of your everyday eating.

 ProPoints values per serving
ProPoints values per recipe 19

 Serves 4
Takes 30 minutes

100 g (3½ oz) quinoa, rinsed
2 teaspoons vegetable stock powder
100 g (3½ oz) couscous
1 red onion, finely chopped
¼ cucumber, finely chopped
100 g (3½ oz) ready-prepared
    pomegranate seeds
2 oranges
a handful of fresh mint leaves
freshly ground black pepper

1 Put the rinsed quinoa into a saucepan and cover with plenty of cold water. Bring to the boil, then add the vegetable stock powder. Reduce the heat and simmer for 15–20 minutes, until tender. Drain, rinse with cold water and drain well.

2 Meanwhile, put the couscous into a heatproof bowl and just cover with boiling water. Stir well and leave for 15 minutes to swell.

3 Add the quinoa to the couscous with the onion, cucumber and pomegranate seeds. Season with a little black pepper.

4 Use a sharp, serrated knife to remove all the peel and pith from the oranges, doing this over the bowl of couscous to catch all the juice. Cut them into segments, removing all the pith. Stir them through gently, so that they don't break up.

5 Cover and chill the salad until ready to eat, then serve, scattered with mint leaves.

Variation Add a handful of halved grapes or chopped apple to bulk out the salad – without adding any extra **ProPoints** values.

Following the Filling & Healthy day approach?
For this recipe use 2 of your weekly **ProPoints** allowance per serving.

ProPoints values to spare?

+1 by drizzling 1 teaspoon of toasted sesame oil over each portion.

+1 per portion by crumbling 70 g (2½ oz) of reduced fat feta cheese into the salad.

+1 by sprinkling 5 chopped cashew nuts over each portion.

HAM, LEEK
and Red Pepper Tarts

Forget pastry – these savoury tarts are baked without a crust to help keep the *ProPoints* values low.

 ProPoints values per serving 2
ProPoints values per recipe 9

Serves 6
Takes 25 minutes

calorie controlled cooking spray
12 x 15 g (½ oz) thin slices roast ham
1 small carrot or courgette, grated
1 small leek, sliced finely
50 g (1¾ oz) roasted red pepper from a jar, packed in brine, drained, rinsed and chopped
½ teaspoon mixed dried herbs
1 large egg, beaten
salt and freshly ground black pepper

1 Preheat the oven to Gas Mark 5/190°C/fan oven 170°C.

2 Spray 6 holes of a muffin tin with the cooking spray. Use 2 slices of ham to line each hole, pushing them in carefully to avoid breaking them.

3 Mix together the carrot or courgette, leek, roasted red pepper and herbs. Add the beaten egg and season with a little salt and pepper. Mix well.

4 Spoon the mixture into the ham cases, then bake for 15–20 minutes until set. Carefully ease them out of the muffin tin and serve warm or cold.

Cook's tip Use fresh red pepper, just chop it finely first.

Variation Use 4 chopped spring onions instead of the leek.

Following the Filling & Healthy day approach? You don't need to use any of your weekly *ProPoints* allowance for a serving of this recipe.

ProPoints values to spare?

+1 by sprinkling each tart with 2 teaspoons of finely grated Parmesan cheese.

+1 by serving each tart with a 20 g (¾ oz) slice of calorie controlled bread.

+1 by serving each tart with a 10 g (¼ oz) rye crispbread.

MIDWEEK CHICKEN
Roast

This one-pot roast is perfect for a fuss-free meal. I cook it quite often for the family as it's so easy.

 ProPoints values per serving
ProPoints values per recipe 31

Serves 4
Takes 50 minutes

400 g (14 oz) Charlotte or small new potatoes, scrubbed and halved
500 g (1 lb 2 oz) Chantenay or small carrots, halved lengthways
2 parsnips, quartered
½ swede or celeriac, cut into 2 cm (¾ inch) chunks
2 teaspoons vegetable oil
4 x 165 g (5¾ oz) skinless, boneless chicken breasts
4 sprigs fresh thyme, plus extra to garnish
1 courgette, cut into chunks
4 small bunches of cherry tomatoes on the vine
salt and freshly ground black pepper

1 Preheat the oven to Gas Mark 6/200°C/fan oven 180°C.

2 Put the potatoes into a large roasting tin with the carrots, parsnips, and swede or celeriac. Add the oil and toss to coat. Roast for 10 minutes.

3 Meanwhile, cut a pocket in the side of each chicken breast and tuck a sprig of thyme into each one.

4 Add the courgette chunks to the roasting tin, stirring them in. Arrange the chicken breasts on top. Season and roast for a further 30–35 minutes, adding the cherry tomato bunches for the final 5 minutes. Serve garnished with extra thyme.

Variation Use 8 x 80 g (3 oz) chicken thighs instead of breasts, making sure you use skinless, boneless ones. *ProPoints* values per serving will be 10.

Following the Filling & Healthy day approach?
For this recipe use 1 of your weekly *ProPoints* allowance per serving.

ProPoints values to spare?

+1 per portion by making 300 ml (10 fl oz) gravy, using 4 heaped teaspoons of instant gravy granules for chicken, and sharing between the plates.

"I USE COOKED *carrot instead of rice* AS A BASE WHEN I HAVE CHICKEN IN A SAUCE OR BOLOGNESE. IT TASTES JUST AS GOOD AND *fills you up.*"

Jacqui Rodgers Weight Watchers member

COMFORT Food

PROPOINTS VALUES

MARVELLOUS
Minestrone

This soup is brilliant because it really fills you up and it feels like a meal in itself – yet the *ProPoints* values are really low.

 2 *ProPoints* values per serving
ProPoints values per recipe 13

 Serves 6
Takes 45 minutes

1 large onion, chopped
2 garlic cloves, crushed
2 large carrots, chopped
3 celery sticks, sliced thinly
½ swede or celeriac, chopped
1.5 litres (2¾ pints) vegetable stock
410 g can borlotti or cannellini beans
 in water, drained
400 g can chopped tomatoes
2 tablespoons tomato purée
1 tablespoon dried mixed Italian
 herbs
50 g (1¾ oz) dried small pasta shapes
100 g (3½ oz) fine green beans,
 trimmed and sliced
salt and freshly ground black pepper
fresh basil leaves, to garnish

1 Put the onion, garlic, carrots, celery, swede or celeriac, stock, canned beans, tomatoes, tomato purée and dried herbs in a large lidded saucepan.

2 Bring up to the boil, stirring occasionally. Partially cover, then reduce the heat and simmer for 20–25 minutes, until the vegetables are tender.

3 Add the pasta shapes and fine green beans. Stir well, then cook for a further 8–10 minutes, until the pasta is tender. Season, then serve, garnished with basil leaves.

Cook's tip Take a portion of soup to work with you for a healthy packed lunch. Transport it in a wide-necked thermos flask or use a tight-lidded polythene box and reheat in a microwave.

Variation Vary the vegetables as you wish. You could use a courgette instead of the celery.

Following the Filling & Healthy day approach?
For this recipe use 1 of your weekly *ProPoints* allowance per serving.

ProPoints values to spare?

+2 by sprinkling each portion with 1 tablespoon of finely grated Parmesan cheese.

+2 per portion for non-vegetarians by adding 115 g (4¼ oz) sliced chorizo sausage to the soup when you add the pasta.

CREAMY VEGETABLE *Soup*

Simple – yet so good. Just by adding some skimmed milk and thickening the soup slightly, you'll get a gloriously creamy texture.

 ProPoints values per serving
ProPoints values per recipe 11

 Serves 6
Takes 35 minutes

1 large **onion**, sliced
2 large **carrots**, cubed
1 small **swede**, cubed
400 g (14 oz) **celeriac**, cubed
1.5 litres (2¾ pints) vegetable stock
1 tablespoon chopped **fresh herbs**
    (or 1 teaspoon mixed dried herbs)
2 tablespoons cornflour
200 ml (7 fl oz) **skimmed milk**
100 g (3½ oz) frozen or canned
    sweetcorn
salt and freshly ground black pepper
chopped **fresh thyme** or **parsley**, to
    garnish

1 Put the onion, carrots, swede and celeriac into a large lidded saucepan with the stock and herbs. Simmer for 25–30 minutes, partially covered, until the vegetables are tender.

2 Blend the cornflour with 4 tablespoons of the milk, then stir it into the saucepan with the rest of the milk. Add the sweetcorn and bring the soup to the boil, stirring, until thickened.

3 Season and serve, garnished with thyme or parsley. Cool any leftover soup, then store in the fridge in a covered container for up to 4 days, reheating thoroughly when required.

Cook's tips To freeze the soup, cool quickly, pack into 'pour 'n' store' bags or freezer boxes and freeze for up to 3 months.

If you prefer a smooth soup, blend it in a food processor, or use a hand-held blender to purée it in the saucepan.

Variation Use frozen **peas** instead of sweetcorn. **ProPoints** values per serving will be 2.

Following the Filling & Healthy day approach?
For this recipe use 1 of your weekly *ProPoints* allowance per serving.

ProPoints values to spare?

+1 by swirling 1 tablespoon of single cream on to each portion before serving.

+2 by serving each portion with a 40 g (1½ oz) slice brown Irish soda bread or a 30 g (1¼ oz) mini pitta.

+3 by serving each portion with a 50 g (1¾ oz) brown, granary or wholemeal roll.

LEEK AND POTATO
Soup

There's nothing quite like a classic leek and potato soup to warm you up – one of my all-time favourites.

 ProPoints values per serving
ProPoints values per recipe 15

 Serves 4
Takes 35 minutes

2 large **leeks**, sliced
450 g (1 lb) **potatoes**, cut into chunks
1.2 litres (2 pints) vegetable stock
125 g (4½ oz) low fat soft cheese with garlic and herbs
2 tablespoons **skimmed milk**
salt and freshly ground black pepper
1 tablespoon snipped **fresh chives**, to garnish

1 Put the leeks, potatoes and stock into a large lidded saucepan. Bring to the boil, then reduce the heat, cover and simmer for about 25 minutes – or until the vegetables are tender.

2 Purée half the soup in a blender or food processor, or use a hand-held stick blender, adding 100 g (3½ oz) of the soft cheese. Stir in the unblended soup and reheat gently. Season to taste.

3 Mix the remaining soft cheese with the skimmed milk to give a smooth consistency.

4 Ladle the soup into warm bowls and top each portion with a swirl of the soft cheese mixture. Sprinkle with chives and extra black pepper before serving.

Cook's tip If you've only got plain low fat soft cheese, use that – the soup will still taste superb.

Variation Try using 2 large **onions** instead of the leeks and add 1 crushed **garlic clove**.

> *Following the Filling & Healthy day approach?*
> For this recipe use 1 of your weekly **ProPoints** allowance per serving.

ProPoints values to spare?

+1 by sprinkling 1 tablespoon of ready-made croûtons over each portion.

+2 by serving each portion with 2 rye crispbreads.

+3 by serving each portion with a 45 g (1½ oz) piece of French stick.

BAKED AUBERGINE
Parmigiana

Enjoy this classic Italian dish at home rather than in a restaurant. It's the perfect vegetarian supper for two and it doesn't take long at all to make.

 ProPoints values per serving
ProPoints values per recipe 10

 Serves 2
Takes 35 minutes

2 medium aubergines, sliced thinly
calorie controlled cooking spray
1 garlic clove, halved
350 g jar low fat tomato and basil
    pasta sauce
2 tablespoons fresh white
    breadcrumbs
2 tablespoons finely grated Parmesan
    cheese
salt and freshly ground black pepper
fresh basil leaves, to garnish

1 Preheat the grill. Arrange the aubergine slices on a baking sheet and mist them with the cooking spray. Grill for 2–3 minutes on each side, until softened.

2 Preheat the oven to Gas Mark 5/190°C/fan oven 170°C.

3 Rub the cut garlic clove around the insides of 2 gratin dishes (or 1 larger dish) to give a hint of flavour. Discard the garlic.

4 Spoon half the pasta sauce into the base of the dishes. Arrange the aubergine slices on top, season, then spoon the rest of the pasta sauce over them. Mix together the breadcrumbs and Parmesan cheese, then sprinkle evenly over the surface of each dish. Bake for 20–25 minutes, until golden brown and bubbling. Serve scattered with basil leaves.

Variation You could use courgettes instead of aubergines – just slice them lengthways.

Following the Filling & Healthy day approach?
For this recipe use 5 of your weekly **ProPoints** allowance per serving.

ProPoints values to spare?

+1 by sprinkling each portion with an extra 2 teaspoons of finely grated Parmesan cheese.

+2 by adding 40 g (1½ oz) of thinly sliced light mozzarella to each portion, arranging it on top of the aubergine slices.

+3 by serving a 40 g (1½ oz) slice of ciabatta with each portion.

LEEK, PEA AND PARSLEY
Risotto

Curl up on the sofa with a comforting bowl of creamy risotto.

9 *ProPoints* values per serving
ProPoints values per recipe 36

V Serves 4
Takes 35 minutes

calorie controlled cooking spray
300 g (10½ oz) dried risotto rice
3 leeks, sliced thinly
150 ml (5 fl oz) dry white wine
1.2 litres (2 pints) vegetable stock
2 tablespoons chopped fresh parsley
2 teaspoons finely grated lemon zest
200 g (7 oz) frozen petits pois or
   garden peas, thawed
fresh basil leaves, to garnish
   (optional)

1 Heat a large non-stick frying pan or sauté pan and spray with the cooking spray. Add the rice and leeks. Cook over a low heat for 1–2 minutes, stirring, without letting the rice go brown.

2 Pour in the wine and let it bubble up, then add about one-third of the stock. Cook the risotto over a low heat, stirring often, until the liquid has almost been absorbed.

3 Gradually add the remaining stock and continue to cook gently until all the liquid has been absorbed, and the rice is swollen and tender, adding a little more stock or water, if necessary.

4 Stir in the parsley, lemon zest and peas. Cook, stirring occasionally, for another 2–3 minutes, then serve garnished with basil leaves, if liked.

Variation When asparagus is in season, you could try using half leeks and half asparagus.

Following the Filling & Healthy day approach?
For this recipe use 8 of your weekly *ProPoints* allowance per serving.

ProPoints values to spare?

+2 by sprinkling each portion with 1 tablespoon of finely grated Parmesan cheese.

+3 by serving each portion with a 45 g (1½ oz) piece of French stick.

FISH FINGER
Sarnie

This is one of the yummiest comfort foods around and everyone who was at the photo shoot for this just loved the home-made tartare sauce.

 ProPoints values per serving 7
ProPoints values per recipe 15

Serves 2
Takes 20 minutes

4 fish fingers
25 g (1 oz) low fat soft cheese
2 tablespoons 0% fat Greek yogurt
1 tablespoon chopped fresh parsley
2 gherkins in brine, drained and
    chopped finely
2 teaspoons capers in brine, drained
    and chopped
2 x 50 g (1¾ oz) wholemeal rolls
shredded lettuce
1 large tomato, sliced
a squeeze of lemon juice
salt and freshly ground black pepper

1 Preheat the grill. Arrange the fish fingers on the grill rack and cook for 12–15 minutes, turning once.

2 While the fish fingers are cooking, mix together the low fat soft cheese, yogurt, parsley, gherkins and capers.

3 Split the rolls and lightly toast the cut sides. Spread with the tartare sauce, then pile some shredded lettuce on to the bases. Top with the tomato slices and fish fingers. Squeeze some lemon juice over them, and season with a little salt and black pepper. Sandwich the rolls together and serve.

Variation Instead of gherkins and capers, add a little finely grated lemon zest to the soft cheese mixture.

Use white rolls if you'd rather – though they won't contain as much fibre. **ProPoints** values per portion will be the same.

Following the Filling & Healthy day approach?
For this recipe use 7 of your weekly **ProPoints** allowance per serving.

ProPoints values to spare?

+1 by serving 2 tablespoons of tomato ketchup with each portion.

+2 by adding an extra fish finger to each roll.

GRILLED LEMON SALMON
with Leek and Caper Mash

This is a smart and simple dish, with really great flavours.

 ProPoints values per serving
ProPoints values per recipe 21

Serves 2
Takes 30 minutes

400 g (14 oz) potatoes, peeled and
    cut into chunks
1 large leek, sliced finely
2 x 125 g (4½ oz) skinless, boneless
    salmon fillets
calorie controlled cooking spray
finely grated zest and juice of 1 small
    lemon
2 tablespoons skimmed milk
1 tablespoon capers in brine, drained
2 tablespoons chopped fresh parsley
salt and freshly ground black pepper

1 Cook the potatoes in boiling water for 20 minutes, until tender, adding the leek to the saucepan 5 minutes before the end of cooking time.

2 When the potatoes have been cooking for 15 minutes, start to prepare the salmon. Heat a non-stick frying pan and spray with the cooking spray. Add the salmon fillets and cook over a high heat for 2 minutes, then turn them over and cook for a further 2 minutes. Add the lemon zest and juice, cook for another 2 minutes, then turn off the heat and let the salmon rest for a few minutes while you make the mash. Take care not to overcook the salmon – when it's ready, the flesh will be opaque and should flake easily.

3 Drain the potatoes and leeks, reserve a few leeks for the garnish, if liked, then mash them thoroughly. Beat in the milk, then stir in the capers and parsley. Season with black pepper, then reheat briefly.

4 Share the mash between 2 warmed plates and serve with the salmon fillets. Garnish with the reserved leek, if using.

Variation Use smoked or unsmoked haddock or cod fillets instead of salmon. As these are not oil-rich fish, **ProPoints** values per serving will be reduced to 7.

Following the Filling & Healthy day approach? You don't need to use any of your weekly **ProPoints** allowance for a serving of this recipe.

ProPoints values to spare?

+1 by topping each portion of cooked salmon with 2 teaspoons of half fat crème fraîche.

+3 by enjoying a 125 ml (4 fl oz) glass of crisp, dry white wine with your meal.

"*Make beetroot crisps.*

Thinly slice raw beetroot (I use my food processor for this) and then lay them in one layer on a baking sheet that has been sprayed with calorie controlled cooking spray. Sprinkle the beetroot with salt and spray over a little more oil. Put them in a preheated oven, Gas Mark 4/180°C/fan oven 160°C, and cook until the beetroot is completely dried out and crisp. A really tasty alternative to crisps."

Jenny Allwood Weight Watchers member

"ALWAYS HAVE CALORIE CONTROLLED COOKING SPRAY TO HAND, FEWER CALORIES THAN OIL AND DOES THE JOB JUST AS WELL!"

Lisa Pitt
Weight Watchers member

"*Put mini chicken fillets in a food bag,* add dry seasoning – jerk, paprika or whatever takes your fancy – and shake. Put the coated fillets on a baking tray in the oven for 20 minutes or until cooked. Really tasty."

Sandra Ali Weight Watchers member

"Take 2 squares of filo pastry and place some sliced cooked pears in the middle, adding 1 cube of dark chocolate, if liked. Scrunch and twist up all the edges, spray with calorie controlled cooking spray and bake for 10 minutes or until lightly brown. Scrummy!"

Alison Pratlett Weight Watchers member

"I SWAP TAKEAWAY PIZZA FOR WEIGHT WATCHERS NAAN BREADS SPREAD WITH PASSATA, AND TOPPED WITH WEIGHT WATCHERS CHEESE, WEIGHT WATCHERS HAM, AND MUSHROOMS. THE KIDS LOVE MAKING THEM, THEY'RE CHEAPER AND ARE FEWER PROPOINTS VALUES."

Stacey Leadeham
Weight Watchers member

STEAK & PEPPER
Goulash

This slow-cook heart-warming casserole is the ultimate comfort food.

 6 *ProPoints* values per serving
ProPoints values per recipe 23

 Serves 4
Preparation time 25 minutes
Cooking time 1½ hours

calorie controlled cooking spray
500 g (1 lb 2 oz) lean braising steak,
  cut into chunks
1 tablespoon ground paprika
2 onions, sliced
2 garlic cloves, crushed
2 carrots, sliced
1 red pepper, de-seeded and
  chopped
1 green pepper, de-seeded and
  chopped
2 x 400 g cans chopped tomatoes
2 tablespoons tomato purée
300 ml (10 fl oz) beef stock
2 tablespoons cornflour
salt and freshly ground black pepper

1 Preheat the oven to Gas Mark 4/180°C/fan oven 160°C.

2 Heat a large flameproof casserole dish and spray with the cooking spray. Add the beef, a handful at a time, cooking over a high heat until sealed and browned – about 2–3 minutes.

3 Add the paprika, onions and garlic and cook, stirring, for 1–2 minutes. Then add the carrots, peppers, tomatoes, tomato purée and stock.

4 Cover the casserole dish and transfer to the oven. Cook for 1½ hours, or until the meat is very tender. Check the liquid level occasionally, adding a little water if needed.

5 Lift the casserole dish on to the hob. Blend the cornflour with 3 tablespoons of cold water, then add to the goulash and stir over a low heat until thickened. Season to taste then serve.

Cook's tip To freeze, cool the goulash quickly, pack into a suitable freezer container and freeze for up to 2 months.

Variation You could make the goulash with lean pork shoulder instead of beef. *ProPoints* values per serving would be 5.

Following the Filling & Healthy day approach?
For this recipe use 1 of your weekly *ProPoints* allowance per serving.

ProPoints values to spare?

+1 by topping each portion with 1 tablespoon of half fat crème fraîche.

PORK
Saltimbocca

The Parma ham wrapped around the pork gives this dish a delicious flavour – a quick and easy midweek meal.

 10 *ProPoints* values per serving
ProPoints values per recipe 40

Serves 4
Takes 25 minutes

600 g (1 lb 5 oz) new potatoes,
    scrubbed
450 g (1 lb) lean pork fillet, trimmed
8 fresh sage leaves
8 slices Parma ham
calorie controlled cooking spray
4 tablespoons Marsala or dry sherry
100 ml (3½ fl oz) vegetable stock
400 g (14 oz) carrots, sliced thinly
300 g (10½ oz) fine green beans
salt and freshly ground black pepper

1 Put the potatoes on to cook in plenty of boiling water.

2 Slice the pork fillet into 8, cutting at a steep angle to get larger, thinner slices. Flatten the slices slightly and place a sage leaf on top of each one. Season with a little black pepper, then wrap each piece with a slice of Parma ham.

3 Heat a large non-stick frying pan and mist with the cooking spray. Add the Parma-wrapped pork and cook over a medium-high heat for 2 minutes on each side.

4 Pour in the Marsala or sherry and add the stock. Turn the heat to low, then simmer gently for about 8 minutes to reduce the liquid, turning the fillets once.

5 Meanwhile, cook the carrots and green beans in boiling water until just tender – about 5–6 minutes. Serve the pork fillet with the new potatoes, carrots and green beans, spooning the reduced sauce over the top.

Variation You could try using 4 x 125 g (4½ oz) fillets of skinless, boneless cod loin – just reduce the cooking time by 3–4 minutes. *ProPoints* values per serving would be 8.

Following the Filling & Healthy day approach?
For this recipe use 3 of your weekly *ProPoints* allowance per serving.

SPRING LAMB
Stew

Enjoy the flavours of new season lamb with this delicious stew.

 9 *ProPoints* values per serving
ProPoints values per recipe 35

 Serves 4
Preparation time 20 minutes
+ Cooking time 50 minutes

calorie controlled cooking spray
400 g (14 oz) lean lamb leg steaks,
    cut into chunks
8 shallots, halved
8 baby leeks, each cut into
    3–4 pieces
400 g (14 oz) small carrots, halved
    lengthways
400 g (14 oz) small new potatoes,
    scrubbed
1.2 litres (2 pints) vegetable stock
2 tablespoons chopped fresh parsley
100 g (3½ oz) fresh or frozen peas
2 tablespoons cornflour
salt and freshly ground black pepper

1 Spray a large flameproof casserole dish or heavy-based saucepan with the cooking spray. Add the lamb, a handful at a time, and cook over a high heat until sealed and browned – about 3–4 minutes.

2 Add the shallots, leeks, carrots, new potatoes, stock and 1 tablespoon of parsley. Bring to the boil, then reduce the heat and simmer, covered, for 45 minutes.

3 Add the peas to the stew and season to taste.

4 Blend the cornflour with 3 tablespoons of cold water and add to the stew, stirring until thickened. Add the remaining parsley then ladle into 4 warmed bowls and serve.

Cook's tip If you prefer, cook the casserole in the oven for an hour at Gas Mark 5/190°C/fan oven 170°C.

Variation You could use 450 g (1 lb) skinless, boneless chicken breasts – cook them whole with the vegetables, browning them first as in step 1. *ProPoints* values per serving would be 7.

Following the Filling & Healthy day approach?
For this recipe use 6 of your weekly *ProPoints* allowance per serving.

ProPoints values to spare?

+1 per portion by adding 40 g (1½ oz) of pearl barley to the stew with the stock.

CHICKEN
Schnitzel

I love chicken schnitzel and with this recipe you really do get a generous portion.

 10 *ProPoints* values per serving
ProPoints values per recipe 42

Serves 4
Preparation time 20 minutes
    + Cooking time 30 minutes

calorie controlled cooking spray
450 g (1 lb) sweet potatoes, cut into
    wedges
4 x 150 g (5½ oz) skinless, boneless
    chicken breasts
100 g (3½ oz) low fat soft cheese
2 spring onions, finely chopped
1 teaspoon finely chopped fresh red
    chilli (optional)
4 x 30 g (1¼ oz) thin slices roast or
    boiled ham
75 g (2¾ oz) instant polenta
1 egg
freshly ground black pepper
mixed leaf salad or lightly cooked
    fresh vegetables, to serve

1 Preheat the oven to Gas Mark 5/190°C/fan oven 170°C. Spray 2 baking sheets with the cooking spray.

2 Arrange the sweet potato wedges on one of the baking sheets and spray with the cooking spray. Set aside.

3 Place the chicken breasts, spaced apart, on a large piece of cling film. Cover with a second piece of cling film. Use a meat mallet or rolling pin to gently but firmly beat out the chicken breasts until they are about half their original thickness.

4 Mix together the low fat soft cheese, spring onions and chilli (if using) and season with pepper. Spread over one side of each chicken breast, then top with a slice of ham, trimming it to fit.

5 Sprinkle the polenta on to a large plate. Beat the egg with 2 tablespoons of cold water. Brush the ham and chicken with beaten egg, then coat in the polenta. Arrange on the second baking sheet.

6 Bake the chicken and sweet potatoes for 25–30 minutes, until the chicken is tender. Check with a sharp knife inserted into the thickest part – the juices should run clear. Serve with a mixed leaf salad or vegetables.

Cook's tip For a little extra flavour, use low fat soft cheese with garlic and herbs.

Following the Filling & Healthy day approach?
For this recipe use 3 of your weekly *ProPoints* allowance per serving.

SAUSAGE, EGG, CHIPS
and Baked Beans

A fry-up – but without the frying. Perfect for a weekday supper or weekend brunch.

 10 *ProPoints* values per serving
ProPoints values per recipe 40

Serves 4
Takes 40 minutes

450 g (1 lb) potatoes, peeled and cut
    into chips
2 teaspoons vegetable oil
8 Weight Watchers sausages
calorie controlled cooking spray
4 eggs
420 g can reduced sugar and salt
    baked beans
freshly ground black pepper

1 Preheat the oven to Gas Mark 6/200°C/fan oven 180°C.

2 Put the chips into a roasting tin, add the oil and toss to coat. Put the sausages into a separate roasting tin. Roast the sausages and chips for 30–35 minutes, turning them over after 20 minutes. The chips should be golden and tender.

3 A few minutes before the sausages and chips are ready, spray a large non-stick frying pan with the cooking spray. Carefully break in the eggs and cook over a medium heat for 2–3 minutes to set them. At the same time, heat the beans in a saucepan.

4 Turn the oven off and preheat the grill. Share the sausages, chips and beans between 4 warm plates. While doing this, put the frying pan under the grill to set the surface of the eggs. Serve, sprinkled with black pepper.

Cook's tip For extra fibre (and less effort), don't peel the potatoes.

Following a Filling & Healthy day approach?
For this recipe use 4 of your weekly *ProPoints* allowance per serving.

ProPoints values to spare?

+1 by serving 2 tablespoons of tomato ketchup with each portion.

+3 by serving 2 grilled rashers of lean back bacon with each portion.

+3 by serving each portion with 2 x 40 g (1½ oz) slices of calorie controlled bread, toasted.

POTATO AND ONION HOTPOT
with Crispy Bacon

I remember my mother making this dish for my family when I was a child – it's brilliantly cheap and is perfect for a chillier day.

 7 **ProPoints** values per serving
ProPoints values per recipe 28

Serves 4
Preparation time 15 minutes
Cooking time 1¼ hours

1 kg (2 lb 4 oz) floury potatoes, peeled and sliced thinly
2 large onions, sliced thinly
1 litre (1¾ pints) chicken or vegetable stock
8 lean bacon medallions
a few fresh thyme sprigs
salt and freshly ground black pepper

1 Preheat the oven to Gas Mark 5/190°C/fan oven 170°C.

2 Arrange the potato and onion slices in alternate layers in a 2.5 litre (4½ pint) baking dish or casserole dish, seasoning each layer with a little salt and pepper, finishing with a layer of potatoes. Pour in the stock.

3 Transfer to the oven and bake, uncovered, for 1 hour, or until the potatoes are tender. Arrange the bacon medallions on the top with the thyme sprigs and bake for another 15 minutes. The top layer of potatoes and the bacon should be crisp.

4 Share between warmed plates and serve.

Variation **V** For a vegetarian version, leave out the bacon, and use vegetable stock; 15 minutes before the end of cooking time, sprinkle 100 g (3½ oz) vegetarian Cheddar over the surface. **ProPoints** values per portion will be 8.

Following the Filling & Healthy day approach? You don't need to use any of your weekly **ProPoints** allowance for a serving of this recipe.

ProPoints values to spare?

+1 by serving 2 tablespoons of tomato ketchup with each portion – it tastes perfect with the hotpot.

+3 by serving each portion with 2 x 40 g (1½ oz) slices of calorie controlled bread.

"IF YOU FIND FRESH FRUIT GOES OFF TOO QUICKLY OR IS TOO EXPENSIVE, *buy tinned fruit in juice,* DRAIN, THEN DECANT INTO A PLASTIC TUB AND POP INTO THE FRIDGE. GREAT WHEN YOU'RE FEELING PECKISH OR *looking for something sweet.*"

Lynsey Pledger Weight Watchers member

QUICK Fixes

PROPOINTS VALUES

GARDEN PITTA
Pizzas

These vegetarian pizzas are made with pitta bread bases, to help you create something quick, easy and very tasty.

 ProPoints values per serving
ProPoints values per recipe 20

 Serves 4
Takes 25 minutes

400 g can chopped **tomatoes** with herbs
1 small **onion**, chopped finely
1 **garlic clove**, crushed
4 wholemeal pitta breads
1 teaspoon dried mixed Italian herbs
1 small **courgette**, pared into ribbons
100 g (3½ oz) **mushrooms**, sliced thinly
50 g (1¾ oz) frozen **peas**
40 g (1½ oz) half fat Cheddar cheese, grated
freshly ground black pepper
fresh **basil** leaves, to garnish

1 Preheat the oven to Gas Mark 6/200°C/fan oven 180°C.

2 Tip the can of tomatoes into a saucepan and add the onion and garlic. Simmer for 5–8 minutes until reduced and pulpy.

3 Arrange the pitta breads on a baking sheet and share the tomato mixture between them, spreading it out towards the edges. Sprinkle the herbs on top, then share the courgette ribbons, mushrooms and peas between them. Season with black pepper and sprinkle the grated cheese on top.

4 Bake for 10–12 minutes, until piping hot. Serve, garnished with basil leaves.

Cook's tip The easiest way to pare the courgette into ribbons is to use a potato peeler.

Following the Filling & Healthy day approach?
For this recipe use 5 of your weekly **ProPoints** allowance per serving.

ProPoints values to spare?

+1 per portion by sprinkling 10 g (¼ oz) finely grated Parmesan cheese over each pitta with the grated half fat Cheddar.

+2 for non-vegetarians by serving each portion topped with 2 thin slices, 30 g (1¼ oz), of Parma ham.

+2 for non-vegetarians by sprinkling 30 g (1¼ oz) finely chopped chorizo sausage over each pitta before adding the cheese.

SEA BASS WITH FENNEL,
Orange and Cannellini Beans

These fresh flavours go so well together in this speedy supper.

 6 *ProPoints* values per serving
ProPoints values per recipe 26

Serves 4
Takes 20 minutes

calorie controlled cooking spray
1 red onion, chopped finely
1 fennel bulb, sliced thinly
4 x 150 g (5½ oz) sea bass fillets
finely grated zest and juice of 1 small
   lemon
2 x 410 g cans cannellini beans in
   water, one can drained
1 large orange
1 tablespoon chopped fresh parsley
freshly ground black pepper

1 Preheat the grill to medium-high. Spray a large non-stick frying pan with the cooking spray and cook the onion and fennel over a medium-high heat for 5 minutes, until softened.

2 At this point, arrange the fish fillets on the grill rack and sprinkle them with the lemon zest and juice. Season with black pepper. Grill for 6–8 minutes, until cooked.

3 When you start to grill the fish, add the cannellini beans and the liquid from one can to the onion and fennel and bring to the boil, then reduce the heat and simmer for 5–6 minutes, adding a splash of water if needed. Peel the orange with a sharp, serrated knife to remove all the peel and pith, then cut it into segments. Gently stir them into the beans with the parsley, so that you don't break up the segments.

4 Ladle the bean mixture on to 4 warm serving plates and serve with the fish.

Variation Use a couple of tomatoes or a chopped beef tomato instead of the orange.

Following the Filling & Healthy day approach? You don't need to use any of your weekly *ProPoints* allowance for a serving of this recipe.

ProPoints values to spare?

+2 per portion by stirring 150 g (5½ oz) cooked couscous into the cannellini bean mixture.

+2 by serving each portion with a 30 g (1¼ oz) piece of French stick.

ORZO PASTA
and Ham Salad

Orzo pasta is shaped like rice and has a lovely texture. It doesn't take long to cook, making it ideal for this quick and easy salad.

 ProPoints values per serving
ProPoints values per recipe 31

Serves 4
Takes 10 minutes

225 g (8 oz) dried orzo pasta
  (or other small pasta shapes)
1 teaspoon vegetable stock powder
2 tablespoons balsamic vinegar
2 teaspoons olive oil
2 large tomatoes, chopped
½ cucumber, peeled, de-seeded and
  chopped
6 spring onions, chopped finely
200 g (7 oz) thick-cut lean ham,
  chopped
2 tablespoons chopped fresh parsley
freshly ground black pepper
rocket and cherry tomatoes, to serve

1 Cook the orzo pasta in plenty of gently boiling water with the vegetable stock powder stirred through, to add more flavour. It will need about 8 minutes to cook until 'al dente'.

2 While the pasta is cooking, put the vinegar and olive oil into a salad bowl (not a metal one) and add the tomatoes, cucumber and spring onions, stirring gently to mix.

3 Drain the cooked pasta and rinse it with cold water to cool it quickly. When thoroughly drained, add it to the salad bowl with the ham and parsley and stir everything together. Season with black pepper. Cover and chill. Serve with rocket and cherry tomatoes.

Cook's tip Serve as a main course salad, with shredded lettuce or rocket and grated carrot on the side, or spoon into pots to take with you for a packed lunch or picnic.

Variation Drain and flake 2 x 160 g cans of tuna in water and add them to the salad instead of the ham. **ProPoints** values per portion will be 8.

Following the Filling & Healthy day approach?
For this recipe use 6 of your weekly **ProPoints** allowance per serving.

ProPoints values to spare?

+1 per portion by cooking an extra 40 g (1½ oz) of dried pasta – that's 265 g (9¼ oz) in total.

+2 by serving each portion with 40 g (1½ oz) of light mozzarella cheese, sliced thinly.

+3 by serving each portion with a 40 g (1½ oz) slice of ciabatta.

CAULIFLOWER CHEESE *Soup*

Enjoy all the flavours of cauliflower cheese in this quick, creamy soup, topped off with a toasted slice of French bread with melted cheese.

 4 *ProPoints* values per serving
ProPoints values per recipe 15

 Serves 4
Takes 20 minutes

(without bread)

1 litre (1¾ pints) vegetable stock
1 cauliflower, broken into florets
1 bunch of spring onions, chopped
175 g (6 oz) low fat soft cheese
2 tablespoons chopped fresh
    parsley, plus extra, to garnish
4 x 2.5 cm (1 inch) slices French
    bread, weighing 80 g (3 oz) in total
40 g (1½ oz) half fat Cheddar cheese,
    grated
freshly ground black pepper

1 Put the vegetable stock into a large saucepan and bring to the boil. Add the cauliflower and spring onions, then cover and reduce the heat. Simmer for 15 minutes until the cauliflower is tender.

2 Transfer the soup to a blender and add the low fat soft cheese. Blend until smooth. Alternatively use a hand-held stick blender to blend the ingredients in the saucepan. Add the parsley, season with black pepper and reheat gently.

3 Meanwhile, preheat the grill. Toast the French bread on one side, then turn the pieces over and sprinkle the cheese on top. Grill until melted.

4 Ladle the soup into bowls and top each portion with a slice of the toasted French bread. Serve, sprinkled with a little extra black pepper and parsley.

Cook's tip Avoid adding salt to the soup, as the cheese will give the soup all the seasoning it needs.

Variation You could make this soup with broccoli instead of cauliflower; use a large head of broccoli and break it up into small florets. *ProPoints* values per portion will be the same.

Following the Filling & Healthy day approach?
For this recipe use 4 of your weekly *ProPoints* allowance per serving.

HOUMOUS
and Carrot Salad Bruschetta

Add crunch to your lunch with this tasty little number.

5 *ProPoints* values per serving
ProPoints values per recipe 20

 Serves 4
Takes 10 minutes

1 teaspoon poppy seeds
1 teaspoon black onion seeds or
   sesame seeds
1 large **carrot**, grated
2 tablespoons raisins or sultanas
1 tablespoon white wine or cider
   vinegar
15 cm (6 inch) slice French stick,
   weighing 125 g (4½ oz), sliced
   horizontally and halved
calorie controlled cooking spray
75 g (2¾ oz) reduced fat houmous
freshly ground black pepper
fresh coriander sprigs, to garnish

1 First make the carrot salad. Toast the poppy seeds and black onion seeds or sesame seeds in a dry frying pan for 1–2 minutes to release their aroma, stirring them so that they don't burn. Tip them into a bowl and add the carrot and raisins or sultanas, stirring to mix. Add the vinegar and stir again.

2 Wipe out the frying pan with kitchen paper. Spray the cut surfaces of the French stick with the cooking spray, then place them in the frying pan, cut sides down, and brown for 1–2 minutes. Alternatively, heat a char-grill pan and brown the French bread for about 2 minutes to give attractive ridges, or simply toast it under the grill.

3 Spread an equal amount of houmous over each piece of bread, then share the carrot salad between them. Season with black pepper, and garnish with fresh coriander sprigs.

Cook's tip You can keep the carrot salad in a covered container in the fridge for up to 2 days. 1 portion is 1 ***ProPoints*** value.

> *Following the Filling & Healthy day approach?*
> For this recipe use 5 of your weekly ***ProPoints*** allowance per serving.

ProPoints values to spare?

+1 per portion by drizzling 2 teaspoons of toasted sesame oil into the carrot salad.

+1 by sprinkling 1 teaspoon of toasted pine nuts over each portion.

MEXICAN SALSA
Melts

Make these easy quesadillas a regular part of your eating plan – they're so quick and tasty.

 5 **ProPoints** values per serving
ProPoints values per recipe 22

 Serves 4
Takes 10 minutes

calorie controlled cooking spray
4 Weight Watchers soft flour tortillas
150 g (5½ oz) half fat Cheddar
    cheese, grated
2 tomatoes, finely chopped
3 spring onions, finely chopped
¼ cucumber, finely chopped
1 small red or yellow pepper,
    de-seeded and chopped finely
1 tablespoon chopped fresh
    coriander or parsley
freshly ground black pepper

1 Heat a non-stick frying pan and spray with the cooking spray. Add 1 tortilla and sprinkle a quarter of the grated cheese over the surface. Cook over a medium-low heat for about 1 minute to brown the base of the tortilla and melt the cheese. Sprinkle with a quarter of the chopped tomato, spring onions, cucumber and pepper. Snip some coriander or parsley over the top.

2 Season with black pepper, then fold the tortilla in half. Slide on to a plate and serve, cut in half. Repeat with the remaining ingredients to make 4 in total.

Cook's tip It's great to get kids into the habit of healthy eating, and this is an ideal snack for when they arrive home from school – and you can factor in one for yourself, without overloading your *ProPoints* values budget.

Following the Filling & Healthy day approach?
For this recipe use 5 of your weekly *ProPoints* allowance per serving.

ProPoints values to spare?

+1 by drizzling 1 tablespoon (15 g) of sweet chilli sauce over each tortilla before folding in half.

+1 by sharing an extra 50 g (1¾ oz) of grated half fat Cheddar cheese between the portions – 200 g (7 oz) in total.

+1 for non-vegetarians by chopping a 30 g (1¼ oz) slice of premium ham over each tortilla before folding in half.

CHICKEN
Fusilli

Shop-bought pasta salads never taste as good as home-made, and they are often higher in *ProPoints* values. Try this simple recipe instead.

 9 *ProPoints* values per serving
ProPoints values per recipe 19

Serves 2
Takes 12 minutes

125 g (4½ oz) dried fusilli pasta (or other small pasta shapes)
1 teaspoon vegetable stock powder
1 tablespoon red or green pesto
1 small carrot, grated
1 large tomato, chopped
1 small red or yellow pepper, de-seeded and chopped
¼ cucumber, halved lengthways, then sliced
200 g (7 oz) cooked skinless, boneless chicken breasts, chopped
1 tablespoon chopped fresh chives or parsley
freshly ground black pepper

1 Cook the pasta in plenty of gently boiling water with the vegetable stock powder stirred through, to add more flavour. It will need about 10 minutes to cook until 'al dente'.

2 While the pasta is cooking, put the pesto in a salad bowl (not a metal one) and add the carrot, tomato, pepper, cucumber, chicken and chives or parsley, stirring gently to mix.

3 Drain the cooked pasta and rinse it with cold water to cool it quickly. When thoroughly drained, add it to the salad bowl and stir everything together gently. Season with black pepper, then cover and chill until ready to serve.

Cook's tip If you're making this salad for a packed lunch, make it the night before, keeping it chilled in the fridge. It will keep for up to 2 days – so you can spread it out over a couple of lunches for two people.

Variation Drain and flake a 125 g can of mackerel in brine and add to the salad instead of the chicken. *ProPoints* values per portion will be 10.

Following the Filling & Healthy day approach?
For this recipe use 7 of your weekly *ProPoints* allowance per serving.

ProPoints values to spare?

+2 per portion by cooking an extra 40 g (1½ oz) of dried fusilli – 165 g (5¾ oz) in total.

+2 by serving each portion with 1 mini white or wholemeal pitta bread.

CURRIED LAMB PITTAS
with Coriander Raita

Make every mealtime matter by preparing something tasty and satisfying, like these spiced lamb pittas. You'll feel so much better for it.

 8 *ProPoints* values per serving
ProPoints values per recipe 16

Serves 2
Takes 10 minutes

calorie controlled cooking spray
100 g (3½ oz) boneless lamb leg
    steak, thinly sliced
1 small red onion, sliced thinly
1 teaspoon cumin seeds or ground
    cumin
1 teaspoon ground coriander
2 wholemeal or white pitta breads
3 tablespoons 0% fat Greek yogurt
1 tablespoon chopped fresh
    coriander
mixed salad leaves
freshly ground black pepper

1 Heat a non-stick frying pan and spray it with the cooking spray. Add the strips of lamb and stir-fry over a high heat for 3–4 minutes, until browned. Add the red onion and cook for another minute or two, then stir in the cumin and coriander. Set to one side while you warm the pittas.

2 Heat the pittas in a toaster or under the grill, so that they puff up. While they are warming, mix together the yogurt and fresh coriander.

3 Split the pittas open and stuff them with the lamb mixture and salad leaves. Season with black pepper, then serve with the coriander raita spooned on top.

Cook's tip Pittas always need warming before you can split them open, but whether you do this in your toaster or under the grill, don't overcook them – they shouldn't be crisp or brown.

Following the Filling & Healthy day approach?
For this recipe use 7 of your weekly *ProPoints* allowance per serving.

ProPoints values to spare?

+1 per portion by cooking an extra 40 g (1½ oz) of lamb – 140 g (5 oz) in total.

+1 by serving each portion with 1 tablespoon of sweet chilli sauce.

+1 per portion by using 3 tablespoons of half fat crème fraîche instead of the yogurt.

BACON, EGG AND TOMATO *Salad*

Pull this salad together in no time at all – perfect for when you've just got in the door.

ProPoints values per serving
ProPoints values per recipe 14

Serves 2
Takes 20 minutes

2 **eggs**
4 rashers lean back bacon
1 Romaine **lettuce**, shredded
12 cherry **tomatoes**, halved
2 tablespoons lemon juice
2 teaspoons olive oil
1 teaspoon wholegrain mustard
2 tablespoons croûtons
freshly ground black pepper
mustard and cress or fresh chives,
     snipped, to garnish

1 Hard-boil the eggs in simmering water for 12 minutes.

2 Meanwhile, preheat the grill. Arrange the bacon rashers on the grill rack and cook for 4–5 minutes, turning once, until crispy. While the bacon is cooking, share the lettuce and tomatoes between 2 serving plates.

3 Make the dressing by mixing together the lemon juice, olive oil and wholegrain mustard with 1 tablespoon of water. Season with black pepper.

4 When the eggs are cooked, leave them to cool for a few minutes in a bowl of cold water. Shell and quarter them, arranging 4 pieces on each salad. Snip the bacon rashers on top, then sprinkle with the dressing. Scatter the croûtons over the salads and garnish with mustard and cress or chives. Serve at once.

Variation **V** For a vegetarian version, use 40 g (1½ oz) of light halloumi cheese per person instead of the bacon, chopping it up into small pieces and dry-frying it until browned. Then just sprinkle over the salads. **ProPoints** values per serving will be 7.

Following the Filling & Healthy day approach?
For this recipe use 5 of your weekly **ProPoints** allowance per serving.

ProPoints values to spare?

+1 per portion by mixing 2 tablespoons (30 g) of sweet chilli sauce into the dressing, omitting the mustard.

"When cooking don't guesstimate foods with high **ProPoints** values. Your hard work can easily be sabotaged by extra **ProPoints** values points creeping in.*"*

Linzi Mappin Weight Watchers member

"I MAKE MY OWN DIP: MIX SOME CRUSHED CLOVES OF GARLIC (ACCORDING TO TASTE) WITH LOW FAT PLAIN YOGURT – A 150 G POT IS FILLING & HEALTHY AND ONLY 2 PROPOINTS VALUES. PERFECT FOR SOME NIGHT-TIME NIBBLING WITH CARROTS OR WEIGHT WATCHERS CRISPS."

Sheryl MacDonald
Weight Watchers member

"Buy pre-prepared, so when you have days when you need a quick meal you have the staples without the fuss."

Kim Ball Weight Watchers member

"USE LETTUCE LEAVES INSTEAD OF TORTILLAS TO MAKE WRAPS."

Tracy Colville
Weight Watchers member

"FREEZE FRESH HERBS IN ICE CUBE TRAYS TO KEEP THEM FOR LONGER. THEN YOU CAN JUST ADD THEM STRAIGHT TO THE POT FOR EXTRA FLAVOUR."

Hannah Syms
Weight Watchers member

ALLOTMENT
Frittata

Use up leftover cooked potatoes in this really easy frittata.

ProPoints values per serving **4**
ProPoints values per recipe 22

V Serves 6

Takes 20 minutes + cooling

❄

calorie controlled cooking spray

1 onion, chopped

1 large courgette, sliced

300 g (10½ oz) cooked new
    potatoes, chopped into chunks

75 g (2¾ oz) frozen petits pois or
    garden peas

2 handfuls of baby spinach leaves

6 eggs

3 tablespoons skimmed milk

50 g (1¾ oz) mature Cheddar cheese,
    grated

freshly ground black pepper

salad leaves, to garnish

1 Preheat the grill. Heat a non-stick frying pan measuring about 30 cm (12 inches) in diameter and spray with the cooking spray. Add the onion, courgette and potatoes and cook on the hob for 4–5 minutes, stirring often. Add the peas and spinach and cook for 2–3 more minutes to wilt the spinach leaves.

2 Beat the eggs and milk together, season with black pepper, then pour into the frying pan. Cook over a medium-low heat for 4–5 minutes to set the base, then sprinkle the cheese on top. Transfer to the grill to set the surface for about 4–5 minutes. Remove from the heat and cool for 5–10 minutes, so that the frittata will be easier to slice.

3 Cut the frittata into 6 and serve, garnished with salad leaves.

Cook's tip Use a good non-stick frying pan so that the frittata is easy to remove.

Following the Filling & Healthy day approach?
For this recipe use 1 of your weekly **ProPoints** allowance per serving.

ProPoints values to spare?

+2 for non-vegetarians by serving each portion topped with 34 g (1¼ oz) of Parma ham – that's 2 thin slices.

GNOCCHI
with Roasted Peppers, Peas and Parmesan

When you need to get supper on the table as fast as possible, this dish is a lifesaver.

 8 *ProPoints* values per serving
ProPoints values per recipe 32

Serves 4
Takes 15 minutes

calorie controlled cooking spray
1 bunch of spring onions, sliced
   thinly
150 g (5½ oz) roasted peppers from a
   jar, packed in brine, sliced
100 g (3½ oz) frozen petits pois or
   garden peas
500 g packet ready-to-cook gnocchi
150 g (5½ oz) ricotta cheese
40 g (1½ oz) Parmesan cheese, finely
   grated
freshly ground black pepper
fresh basil leaves, to garnish

1 Heat a non-stick frying pan and spray with the cooking spray. Gently fry the spring onions for 3–4 minutes, then add the peppers and peas, cooking over a low heat for 1–2 minutes.

2 Meanwhile, bring a large saucepan of water to simmering point. Add the gnocchi and cook gently for 1–2 minutes, until they rise to the surface.

3 Drain the gnocchi, then tip them back into the saucepan and add the spring onions, peppers and peas, stirring gently to mix. Share between 4 warm serving bowls or plates.

4 Divide the ricotta between the portions and sprinkle an equal amount of Parmesan cheese on to each one. Season with black pepper, then serve, garnished with basil leaves.

Cook's tip Take care that you don't overcook the gnocchi – follow the instructions on the packet to get the timing right.

Variation To add more vegetables, pare a courgette into ribbons using a potato peeler and cook with the gnocchi.

Following the Filling & Healthy day approach?
For this recipe use 8 of your weekly *ProPoints* allowance per serving.

ProPoints values to spare?

+2 for non-vegetarians by serving each portion with 2 thin slices, 30 g (1¼ oz), of Parma ham, torn into pieces and stirred into the cooked gnocchi.

HOT ROAST CHICKEN
Salad

Pick up a hot roast chicken on your way home from the shops and prepare a speedy salad with celery, fruit and quinoa.

 10 *ProPoints* values per serving
ProPoints values per recipe 39

Serves 4
Takes 25 minutes

200 g (7 oz) quinoa
600 ml (20 fl oz) vegetable stock
400 g (14 oz) hot roast chicken
(skinless and boneless)
3 celery sticks, sliced
1 apple, cored and chopped
200 g (7 oz) seedless grapes, halved
40 g (1½ oz) sultanas or raisins
2 tablespoons lemon juice
freshly ground black pepper
fresh mint or parsley, to garnish

1 Put the quinoa into a saucepan with the vegetable stock. Simmer for 18–20 minutes until the grains are swollen and the liquid has been absorbed.

2 Tip the cooked quinoa into a salad bowl and leave to cool for a few minutes.

3 Tear the chicken into pieces, adding them to the salad bowl. Stir in the celery, apple, grapes, sultanas or raisins, and lemon juice. Season with pepper, then serve, garnished with mint or parsley.

Cook's tip You could use cold chicken left over from a Sunday roast.

Variations Add extra vegetables and fruit to the salad to bulk it up more, such as chopped cooked green beans and slices of fresh orange.

Substitute long grain rice, small pasta shapes or couscous for the quinoa. All *ProPoints* values per serving would be 10.

Following the Filling & Healthy day approach?
For this recipe use 5 of your weekly *ProPoints* allowance per serving.

ProPoints values to spare?

+1 per portion by stirring 2 tablespoons of French dressing through the salad.

+2 per portion by adding an avocado to the salad.

+3 by serving each portion with a 50 g (1¾ oz) soft brown, wholemeal or granary roll.

MOROCCAN-SPICED
Turkey Steaks

Turkey steaks are economical and very tasty – and they're low in fat, making them a good choice.

 ProPoints values per serving 9
ProPoints values per recipe 37

Serves 4
Takes 20 minutes

finely grated zest and juice of 1 small
    lemon
4 teaspoons harissa paste
4 x 150 g (5½ oz) turkey steaks
150 g (5½ oz) couscous
200 ml (7 fl oz) boiling water
410 g can chick peas in water,
    drained
8 radishes, sliced
¼ cucumber, chopped finely
2 tablespoons chopped fresh parsley
1 tablespoon chopped fresh mint,
    plus extra leaves, to garnish
freshly ground black pepper

1 Preheat a char-grill pan or the grill. Mix the lemon juice and harissa paste together, then brush over the turkey steaks. Char-grill or grill them for 8–10 minutes, turning once.

2 Meanwhile, put the lemon zest and couscous into a heatproof bowl and add the boiling water. Stir, then leave to soak and swell for about 5–8 minutes.

3 While the couscous is soaking, mix together the chick peas, radishes, cucumber, parsley and mint.

4 Fluff up the couscous with a fork and stir it into the chick pea mixture. Season with black pepper, then share between 4 plates and serve with the turkey steaks. Scatter each portion with a few mint leaves, to garnish.

Variation You could use 4 x 165 g (5¾ oz) skinless, boneless chicken breasts instead. Flatten them first by placing them between 2 large pieces of cling film and beating them with a meat mallet or rolling pin. **ProPoints** values per portion would be 10.

Following the Filling & Healthy day approach?
For this recipe use 4 of your weekly **ProPoints** allowance per serving.

ProPoints values to spare?

+1 by sprinkling 5 g of toasted pine nuts over each portion.

+2 by serving each portion with a 30 g (1¼ oz) mini white or wholemeal pitta bread.

+3 by crumbling 40 g (1½ oz) of feta cheese over each portion.

QUICK BEEF AND PEPPER
Noodles

Vibrant colours, delicious textures and great flavours make this a truly tasty stir-fry.

 ProPoints values per serving
ProPoints values per recipe 23

Serves 4
Takes 15 minutes

4 tablespoons orange juice
2 tablespoons soy sauce
2 tablespoons oyster sauce
1 teaspoon cornflour
calorie controlled cooking spray
300 g (10½ oz) lean rump steak, sliced thinly
1 bunch of spring onions, sliced thinly
1 red pepper, de-seeded and thinly sliced
1 yellow pepper, de-seeded and thinly sliced
150 g (5½ oz) mangetout or sugarsnap peas, halved
300 g packet udon straight-to-wok noodles
freshly ground black pepper

1 Mix together the orange juice, soy sauce, oyster sauce and cornflour in a small bowl, stirring until smooth. Set aside.

2 Heat a wok or large frying pan and spray with the cooking spray. Add the beef and stir-fry over a high heat for 2 minutes, then add the spring onions, peppers and mangetout or sugarsnap peas and stir-fry for another 4–5 minutes, until the vegetables are cooked, yet still crunchy.

3 Tip the noodles into the wok and stir gently to distribute them. Stir the cornflour mixture, then add it to the wok and stir until slightly thickened. Season with black pepper, then share between 4 warm serving plates or bowls.

Cook's tip To spice up the flavours, add 1 teaspoon of Chinese five spice powder when you add the vegetables.

Variation Use 300 g (10½ oz) of skinless, boneless chicken breasts instead of beef. **ProPoints** values per serving will be 5.

Following the Filling & Healthy day approach?
For this recipe use 3 of your weekly **ProPoints** allowance per serving.

ProPoints values to spare?

+1 by sprinkling 5 roasted cashew nuts over each portion.

+1 by drizzling 1 tablespoon of sweet chilli sauce over each portion.

+1 per portion by adding an extra 175 g (6 oz) of lean rump steak.

GRILLED HADDOCK
with Prawn and Cheddar Topping

Fish is brilliant for speedy, healthy meals. Try to eat it at least once a week – it's not difficult with recipes as tasty as this.

 ProPoints values per serving
ProPoints values per recipe 20

Serves 4
Takes 15 minutes

4 x 150 g (5½ oz) haddock fillets
4 spring onions, finely chopped
150 g (5½ oz) cooked peeled prawns,
   thawed if frozen
50 g (1¾ oz) mature Cheddar cheese,
   grated
freshly ground black pepper
fresh vegetables, to serve

1 Preheat the grill. Arrange the fish fillets on the grill rack and cook them for 3–4 minutes.

2 Scatter the spring onions and prawns over the fish, season with black pepper, then sprinkle the cheese on top. Return to the grill and cook for another 3–4 minutes, so that the cheese melts.

3 Serve with plenty of lightly cooked fresh vegetables.

Cook's tip The time it takes to cook fish varies according to its thickness: if the fillets are thick you may need to cook them for an extra minute or two.

Variation You could use coley, cod or pollock fillets instead of the haddock.

Following the Filling & Healthy day approach?
For this recipe use 1 of your weekly *ProPoints* allowance per serving.

ProPoints values to spare?

+1   per portion by sprinkling an extra 30 g (1¼ oz) grated mature Cheddar cheese over the fish.

WASABI SMOKED SALMON
Wraps

A hint of wasabi paste lifts these salmon tortilla wraps to a new level.

 6 *ProPoints* values per serving
ProPoints values per recipe 13

Serves 2
Takes 15 minutes

100 g (3½ oz) frozen petits pois or
    garden peas
2 teaspoons wasabi paste
1 tablespoon extra light mayonnaise
1 tablespoon 0% fat Greek yogurt
2 Weight Watchers soft flour tortillas
100 g (3½ oz) smoked salmon,
    chopped
shredded lettuce
a few thin slices of cucumber
1 tomato, chopped finely
freshly ground black pepper

1 Cook the peas in boiling water for 2–3 minutes, just to defrost them, then rinse with cold water and drain thoroughly. Use a potato masher or fork to crush them to a rough paste.

2 Add the wasabi paste, mayonnaise and yogurt to the peas and season with some black pepper. Spread over the tortillas, then scatter an equal amount of smoked salmon over each one.

3 Top the tortillas with shredded lettuce, cucumber slices and tomato. Roll up tightly, slice in half, then serve.

Cook's tip Look out for packets of smoked salmon trimmings – they are cheaper to buy and ideal for this recipe.

Variation The mixture makes a great sandwich filling too – use two slices of calorie controlled bread per person instead of the tortillas. *ProPoints* values per serving will be 6.

Following the Filling & Healthy day approach?
For this recipe use 3 of your weekly *ProPoints* allowance per serving.

ProPoints values to spare?

+2 by cubing 40 g (1½ oz) of Brie and sharing it between the tortillas.

+2 by grilling 2 x 20 g (¾ oz) rashers of streaky bacon until crispy, then snipping an equal amount over each portion before rolling up the tortillas.

TUNA, RED ONION
and Mixed Bean Lunch

This is such a great quick fix – it takes minutes to put together and is really tasty.

ProPoints values per serving **5**
ProPoints values per recipe **10**

Serves 2
Takes 15 minutes

150 g (5½ oz) fine green beans,
  chopped
1 small red onion, finely chopped
2 tablespoons lemon juice or vinegar
2 tablespoons tomato purée
40 g (1½ oz) gherkins, chopped finely
1 tablespoon capers, drained
410 g can mixed beans in water,
  drained
12 cherry tomatoes, halved
160 g can tuna in water, drained
freshly ground black pepper
mixed salad leaves, to serve
lemon wedges, to garnish

1 Cook the green beans in boiling water for 4–5 minutes, until just tender.

2 Meanwhile, put the red onion into a bowl with the lemon juice or vinegar, stir well and leave to marinate for 5 minutes. Add the tomato purée, gherkins and capers.

3 Drain the green beans and tip them into the bowl while warm, then add the mixed beans and cherry tomatoes, mixing together thoroughly.

4 Flake the tuna and add to the bean mixture, stirring it in gently to avoid breaking up the chunks too much. Share between two plates and serve with the mixed salad leaves, garnished with lemon wedges and sprinkled with black pepper.

Cook's tip For a delicious lunch on the go, pot up two portions and keep them chilled in a small cool bag with an ice pack until ready to eat.

Variation Add more vegetables to bulk up the salad, making it even more filling without adding any extra *ProPoints* values. A couple of thinly sliced celery sticks and some chopped red or yellow pepper would be perfect.

Following the Filling & Healthy day approach? You don't need to use any of your weekly *ProPoints* allowance for a serving of this recipe.

ProPoints values to spare?

+2 by serving each portion with a 30 g (1¼ oz) mini white or wholemeal pitta.

"*I dip strawberries in fat-free yogurt* AND FREEZE THEM— *a perfect treat* THAT FEELS NAUGHTY BUT ISN'T."

Stephanie Green Weight Watchers member

Guilt-free TREATS

PROPOINTS VALUES

LITTLE CHOCOLATE
Pots

When you can't resist a little sweet something to finish off your meal, indulge in a tiny – yet richly satisfying – pot of chocolate mousse.

6 *ProPoints* values per serving
ProPoints values per recipe 22

V Serves 6
Takes 15 minutes
   + 15 minutes cooling
   + 1 hour chilling

75 g (2¾ oz) dark chocolate
100 ml (3½ fl oz) single cream
2 egg whites

1 Grate a little chocolate for decoration and set aside. Break the rest into pieces and put them into a shallow bowl. Heat the cream in a saucepan until it just begins to boil, then pour it over the chocolate. Leave for 5 minutes without stirring.

2 Mix the cream and chocolate together until smooth. Cool for about 15 minutes, until thickened.

3 Whisk the egg whites in a grease-free bowl until they hold their shape. Add to the chocolate mixture and fold it through gently with a large metal spoon. Share between 6 very small dessert dishes or small espresso cups. Chill for about an hour, until set.

4 Serve, decorated with the grated chocolate.

Variation Dissolve a teaspoon of coffee granules in the cream as you heat it to give a mocha flavour to the desserts.

Following the Filling & Healthy day approach?
For this recipe use 5 of your weekly *ProPoints* allowance per serving.

ProPoints values to spare?

+1 per pudding by adding 28 g (1¼ oz) – that's 4 extra squares – of dark chocolate to the recipe.

+1 by crumbling ½ a low fat digestive biscuit into the base of each dish before adding the chocolate mousse mixture.

CHOCOLATE SPONGE
Puddings

A little taste of heaven.

   ProPoints values per serving
ProPoints values per recipe 24

Serves 6
Preparation time 15 minutes
Cooking time 25 minutes

40 g (1½ oz) low fat spread
40 g (1½ oz) light muscovado sugar
75 g (2¾ oz) self-raising flour
1 tablespoon cocoa powder, plus
    extra, to dust
1 tablespoon skimmed milk
½ teaspoon vanilla extract
1 egg
4 tablespoons half fat crème fraîche,
    to serve
4 strawberries, halved, to decorate

1 Use a tiny amount of the low fat spread to grease 6 castle pudding moulds or ramekins.

2 Put the remaining low fat spread into a mixing bowl with the sugar, flour, cocoa powder, milk and vanilla extract. Crack in the egg, then beat with a wooden spoon for 1 minute, until all the ingredients are combined.

3 Share the mixture between the 6 moulds or ramekins, then place a piece of greased foil on each one, wrapping it tightly around them.

4 Stand the moulds or ramekins in a large lidded saucepan and add enough boiling water to come about one-third of the way up their sides. Cover and steam over a low heat for 25 minutes.

5 Run a knife around the pudding moulds or ramekins and invert to release them. Serve with the crème fraîche and strawberries, and dust with a little cocoa powder.

Cook's tip Check the level of water from time to time to make sure that the saucepan doesn't boil dry – top up with extra boiling water, if needed.

Variation For banana sponge puddings, omit the cocoa powder and add a mashed banana after beating the ingredients together. **ProPoints** values per serving will be 4.

Following the Filling & Healthy day approach?
For this recipe use 4 of your weekly **ProPoints** allowance per serving.

SQUIDGY CARROT
Cake

You'll love this easy-to-make carrot cake.

 5 *ProPoints* values per serving
ProPoints values per recipe 61

 Serves 12
Preparation time 20 minutes
 Cooking time 50 minutes + cooling

100 g (3½ oz) low fat spread
finely grated zest and juice of
  1 large orange, plus extra zest,
  to decorate
2 eggs, beaten
225 g (8 oz) plain flour
1 teaspoon bicarbonate of soda
1 teaspoon baking powder
1 teaspoon ground ginger
150 g (5½ oz) light muscovado sugar
225 g (8 oz) carrots, grated

For the frosting
200 g (7 oz) low fat soft cheese
2 tablespoons icing sugar

1 Preheat the oven to Gas Mark 4/180°C/fan oven 160°C. Grease and line a 20 cm (8 inch) square cake tin with baking paper, using ½ teaspoon of the low fat spread.

2 Melt the remaining spread in a saucepan. Remove the pan from the heat and add the orange juice and beaten eggs. Reserve the orange zest for the frosting.

3 Sift together the flour, bicarbonate of soda, baking powder and ground ginger in a mixing bowl. Stir in the sugar and carrots, then add the melted mixture and stir together well.

4 Turn the mixture into the prepared tin and bake on the middle shelf of the oven for 45–50 minutes, or until a fine skewer inserted into the centre of the cake comes out clean. Cool in the tin for 20 minutes, then turn out carefully and cool completely on a wire rack.

5 Make the frosting by beating together the low fat soft cheese, icing sugar and reserved orange zest. Spread on top of the cooled cake and decorate with orange zest. Cut into 12 equal pieces and keep refrigerated until needed – though the cake is best eaten at room temperature.

Following the Filling & Healthy day approach?
For this recipe use 5 of your weekly *ProPoints* allowance per serving.

ProPoints values to spare?

+1 per square by adding 45 g (1½ oz) ground almonds to the cake mixture with the grated carrots.

+2 per square by using mascarpone cheese instead of low fat soft cheese.

CAPPUCCINO
Crèmes

These are rather like a coffee-flavoured version of crème caramel – and equally delicious.

 ProPoints values per serving
ProPoints values per recipe 16

 Serves 4
Preparation time 15 minutes
Cooking time 30 minutes + chilling

300 ml (10 fl oz) skimmed milk
1 teaspoon vanilla extract
2 teaspoons coffee granules or powder
2 eggs
40 g (1½ oz) caster sugar
3 tablespoons whipping cream
1 teaspoon light muscovado sugar

1 Preheat the oven to Gas Mark 3/160°C/fan oven 140°C. Put the milk in a saucepan with the vanilla extract and coffee granules or powder. Bring to the boil, then remove from the heat and cool for 5–10 minutes.

2 Whisk the eggs and caster sugar together until light and creamy. Add the warm coffee mixture, whisking well.

3 Put 4 glass cups, heatproof dishes or ramekins in a roasting tin. Pour in warm water to come halfway up their sides. Strain the coffee mixture through a fine sieve into the dishes. Bake for 25–30 minutes, until set. Cool, then chill.

4 Whip the cream in a chilled bowl until it holds its shape. Spoon on to the desserts, sprinkle over the muscovado sugar, then serve.

Cook's tip The muscovado sugar dissolves over the cream to give a lovely flavour and finish.

Variation Omit the coffee for plain vanilla-flavoured custards.

Following the Filling & Healthy day approach?
For this recipe use 2 of your weekly *ProPoints* allowance per serving.

ProPoints values to spare?

+1 per pudding by stirring 2 tablespoons of whipping cream into the milk mixture for a creamier result.

+1 by serving each pudding sprinkled with 5 g chopped pistachio nuts or almonds.

STRAWBERRY AND APPLE
Crumbles

More fruit and less crumble helps to keep the *ProPoints* values down.

4 *ProPoints* values per serving
ProPoints values per recipe 16

V

❄

Serves 4
Preparation time 15 minutes
Cooking time 30 minutes

3 Cox's apples, peeled, cored and
  sliced
300 g (10½ oz) strawberries, halved
2 tablespoons lemon juice
40 g (1½ oz) light muscovado sugar
50 g (1¾ oz) plain flour
50 g (1¾ oz) porridge oats
a pinch of salt
40 g (1½ oz) low fat spread

1 Preheat the oven to Gas Mark 4/180°C/fan oven 160°C. Mix together the apples, strawberries, lemon juice and half the sugar. Share between 4 individual ovenproof dishes and sprinkle 1 tablespoon of water into each dish. Stand the dishes on a baking tray and bake for 5 minutes while making the topping.

2 Put the flour, porridge oats and salt into a mixing bowl and add the low fat spread. Rub it in with your fingertips until the mixture looks like crumbs, then stir in the rest of the sugar.

3 Remove the baking dishes from the oven and share the crumble topping between them. Return to the oven and bake for 20–25 minutes, until golden brown.

Cook's tip For a crunchier topping, use demerara sugar instead of muscovado: you need 20 g (¾ oz) sugar for the topping.

Following the Filling & Healthy day approach?
For this recipe use 3 of your weekly *ProPoints* allowance per serving.

ProPoints values to spare?

+1 by serving each crumble with 75 g (2¾ oz) of ready-to-serve low fat custard.

+2 by serving each crumble with a 60 g (2 oz) scoop of low fat vanilla ice cream.

PLUM BEAUTIFUL
Tarts

These lovely little tarts with a hint of almond will go down a treat.

 ProPoints values per serving
ProPoints values per recipe 32

 Serves 8

 Preparation time 20 minutes
Cooking time 25 minutes

calorie controlled cooking spray
6 x 45 g (1½ oz) sheets filo pastry,
   thawed if frozen
1 egg, beaten
50 g (1¾ oz) ground almonds
25 g (1 oz) caster sugar
4 plums, halved, pitted and sliced
   thinly
1 teaspoon icing sugar, to decorate

1 Preheat the oven to Gas Mark 4/180°C/fan oven 160°C. Lightly spray 2 baking sheets with the cooking spray.

2 Unroll the filo pastry sheets, and cut them into 8 equal squares. Arrange on the baking sheet in 8 piles, spraying each layer with a little of the cooking spray, and offsetting the squares as you layer them up to make a rough circle.

3 Reserve 1 tablespoon of beaten egg, then mix the rest with the ground almonds and sugar. Share this mixture between the pastry circles, spreading it in the middle to leave a border round the edge. Top the almond mixture with the sliced plums. Brush the pastry borders with the reserved egg and scrunch up the pastry a little around the filling.

4 Bake for 20–25 minutes, until the pastry is golden brown. Serve the tarts while warm, sprinkled with a little icing sugar.

Cook's tip Keep filo pastry covered with a clean damp cloth until you need it, to prevent it from drying out.

Variation Use small peaches or nectarines instead of plums.

Following the Filling & Healthy day approach?
For this recipe use 4 of your weekly *ProPoints* allowance per serving.

ProPoints values to spare?

+1 by serving each tart with 1 tablespoon of single cream.

+2 by serving each tart with a 60 g (2 oz) scoop of low fat vanilla ice cream.

HOT LEMON SAUCE
Puddings

These lovely little puddings consist of a lively lemon sauce with a light sponge topping.

ProPoints values per serving

ProPoints values per recipe 22

Serves 4
Preparation time 15 minutes
Cooking time 30 minutes

25 g (1 oz) low fat spread, plus
    1 teaspoon, for greasing
75 g (2¾ oz) caster sugar
2 **eggs**, separated
50 g (1¾ oz) plain flour
finely grated zest and juice of
    1 lemon
200 ml (7 fl oz) skimmed milk
1 teaspoon icing sugar, to decorate
    (optional)

1 Preheat the oven to Gas Mark 4/180°C/fan oven 160°C. Grease 4 ramekin dishes with the teaspoon of low fat spread.

2 Beat together the remaining spread with the caster sugar until light and fluffy. Add the egg yolks one at a time, beating well between each addition. Sift in the flour, then add the lemon zest and juice and fold together gently. Stir in the milk. The mixture will be runny and could curdle, but it won't affect the finished pudding.

3 Whisk the egg whites in a grease-free bowl until they hold their shape. Fold them into the lemon mixture, then transfer to the prepared dishes.

4 Stand the dishes on a baking sheet and bake for 25–30 minutes until set and pale golden brown. Cool slightly, then serve, dusted with the icing sugar, if using.

Cook's tip To make absolutely sure that the puddings are 'saucy' at the bottom, stand the dishes in a roasting tin and pour in warm water to come halfway up the sides. This will guarantee they cook gently so that the sauce separates.

Following the Filling & Healthy day approach?
For this recipe use 4 of your weekly *ProPoints* allowance per serving.

ProPoints values to spare?

+1   by serving each pudding with 1 tablespoon of single cream.

+2   by serving each pudding with a 60 g (2 oz) scoop of low fat vanilla ice cream.

"If you fancy something sweet
blitz frozen fruit with a little natural yogurt and it's like
ice cream but with only the *ProPoints* values for your
yogurt. It tastes lovely too! Or you could use a little
milk and have a tasty smoothie!"

Lizzie Taylor Weight Watchers member

"FREEZE GRAPES FOR A SWEET SNACK AND USE BANANAS AS A BASE FOR HOME-MADE ICE CREAM."

Melissa McDonald
Weight Watchers member

"Chocolate Banana.
Slice a banana down the middle
lengthways, put some chocolate
drops in the cut and wrap in foil.
Bake in the oven or over a barbecue
until the chocolate has melted. Low in
ProPoints values and so yummy!"

Sonia Gleed Weight Watchers member

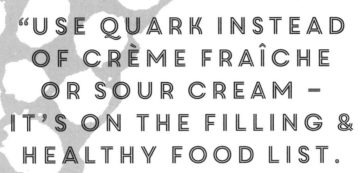

"USE QUARK INSTEAD OF CRÈME FRAÎCHE OR SOUR CREAM – IT'S ON THE FILLING & HEALTHY FOOD LIST. IF YOU BUY THE FIRMER TYPE YOU CAN EASILY SOFTEN IT WITH A LITTLE SKIMMED MILK. I EVEN USE QUARK NOW IN PLACE OF BUTTER OR LOW FAT SPREAD."

Tina Jackson
Weight Watchers member

ORANGE AND CHOCOLATE CHIP
Bread and Butter Pudding

This inspired pudding is a brilliant way to use up bread that's a couple of days old.

 ProPoints values per serving
ProPoints values per recipe 22

 Serves 4
Preparation time 10 minutes
   + 20 minutes soaking
Cooking time 35 minutes

25 g (1 oz) low fat spread
4 slices calorie controlled white bread
25 g (1 oz) dark chocolate chips
1 large orange
2 eggs
450 ml (16 fl oz) skimmed milk
1 teaspoon vanilla extract
20 g (¾ oz) caster sugar

1 Grease a 1.2 litre (2 pint) baking dish with a tiny knob of the low fat spread. Spread the rest on to the slices of bread, then cut each slice into 4 triangles. Arrange them in the dish with the chocolate chips.

2 Finely grate the zest from the orange. Add the eggs, milk and vanilla extract and beat together. Stir in the sugar, allowing a few minutes for it to dissolve. Pour the mixture over the bread, then cover and leave to soak for at least 20 minutes.

3 Preheat the oven to Gas Mark 4/180°C/fan oven 160°C. Peel the orange with a sharp, serrated knife to remove all the pith, then cut into segments.

4 Uncover the pudding and tuck in the orange segments. Bake for about 30–35 minutes, until set and golden brown. Serve warm.

Cook's tip Slightly stale bread works best in this recipe, as its drier texture soaks up more of the egg and milk mixture to give a delicious result.

Following the Filling & Healthy day approach?
For this recipe use 3 of your weekly **ProPoints** allowance per serving.

ProPoints values to spare?

+1 by serving each portion of pudding with 1 tablespoon of single cream.

+2 by serving each portion of pudding with a 60 g (2 oz) scoop of low fat vanilla ice cream.

APPLE AND BLACKBERRY
Cheesecake Sundaes

You get a lovely cheesecake flavour by mixing low fat soft cheese with 0% fat Greek yogurt and adding a little vanilla extract and lemon.

  5 *ProPoints* values per serving
ProPoints values per recipe 9

 V Serves 2
Takes 20 minutes

* 125 g (4½ oz) blackberries
* 1 eating apple, peeled, cored and sliced thinly
* 3 teaspoons caster sugar
* 75 g (2¾ oz) low fat soft cheese
* 4 tablespoons 0% fat Greek yogurt
* ½ teaspoon vanilla extract
* 1 teaspoon finely grated lemon zest
* 1 teaspoon lemon juice
* 2 low fat digestive biscuits, crushed
* blackberry leaves or fresh mint leaves, to decorate (optional)

1 Reserve a few blackberries for decoration, then put the remainder in a small saucepan with the apple, 2 teaspoons of sugar and 5 tablespoons of cold water. Simmer for 10 minutes, stirring occasionally, until the apple is cooked and the liquid has almost evaporated. Leave to cool.

2 Beat together the low fat soft cheese, yogurt, vanilla extract, half the lemon zest, lemon juice and remaining 1 teaspoon of sugar.

3 Layer the crushed biscuits, fruit and soft cheese mixture in 2 pretty serving glasses. Cover and chill until ready to eat, then serve topped with the reserved blackberries and remaining lemon zest, decorated with blackberry or mint leaves, if using.

Cook's tip You could leave out the digestive biscuits to reduce the *ProPoints* values to 3 per serving.

Variation Try using frozen raspberries or mixed summer berries instead of fresh blackberries.

Following the Filling & Healthy day approach?
For this recipe use 4 of your weekly *ProPoints* allowance per serving.

ProPoints values to spare?

+1 by drizzling 1 heaped teaspoon of clear honey over each sundae.

+2 by serving each sundae with a 60 g (2 oz) scoop of low fat vanilla ice cream.

STRAWBERRY MOUSSE
with Smashed Amaretti

This is a lovely light, creamy mousse that sums up the best of fruity summer desserts and is super-low in *ProPoints* values.

ProPoints values per serving 2
ProPoints values per recipe 10

 Serves 6

(if using vegetarian gelatine equivalent)

Takes 30 minutes + 2 hours chilling

11 g sachet powdered gelatine (or vegetarian equivalent)
450 g (1 lb) strawberries
200 g (7 oz) low fat soft cheese
100 g (3½ oz) 0% fat Greek yogurt
20 g (¾ oz) caster sugar
1 teaspoon vanilla extract
2 egg whites
6 amaretti biscuits, to serve
fresh mint leaves, blueberries and edible flowers (if available), to decorate

1 Pour 90 ml (3 fl oz) just-boiled water into a small jug, sprinkle in the gelatine and stir to disperse. Leave for about 10 minutes to dissolve to give a completely clear liquid, stirring occasionally.

2 Meanwhile, reserve a few strawberries for decoration, then purée the rest of them in a blender with the low fat soft cheese, yogurt, caster sugar and vanilla extract.

3 Whisk the egg whites in a large grease-free bowl until they hold their shape, then add the strawberry mixture, and fold in using a large metal spoon. At this point, slowly pour in the liquid gelatine, stirring thoroughly to mix.

4 Transfer the bowl to the fridge and chill until set, about 2 hours.

5 Scoop the strawberry mousse on to serving plates. Serve with crushed amaretti biscuits and decorate with the reserved strawberries, mint leaves, blueberries and edible flowers, if using.

Cook's tip Share the mixture between 6 dessert glasses instead and leave until set.

Following the Filling & Healthy day approach?
For this recipe use 1 of your weekly *ProPoints* allowance per serving.

ProPoints values to spare?

+1 by serving each mousse with 1 tablespoon of half fat crème fraîche.

+1 by serving each mousse with 1 tablespoon of single cream.

MANGO, KIWI AND RASPBERRY
Knickerbocker Glories

You can't beat this classic combination of fruit, ice cream and cream.

ProPoints values per serving **4**
ProPoints values per recipe 17

Serves 4
Takes 15 minutes

300 g (10½ oz) raspberries, thawed
    if frozen
1 large ripe mango, peeled, pitted
    and chopped
1 kiwi fruit, peeled and finely
    chopped
4 tablespoons whipping cream
2 x 12 g meringue nests, roughly
    crushed
4 x 60 g (2 oz) scoops of low fat
    vanilla ice cream

1 Mix the raspberries with the mango and kiwi fruit, reserving 4 raspberries for decoration.

2 Whip the cream in a chilled bowl until it holds its shape.

3 Share half the fruit mixture between 4 sundae glasses. Add the crushed meringue, then top with a scoop of ice cream. Spoon in the rest of the fruit. Share the cream between the portions and serve immediately, decorated with the reserved raspberries.

Cook's tip Chilling the bowl means that cream whips up more successfully – just pop the bowl in the fridge for 20 minutes, or into the freezer for 5 minutes, before you start. For best results use a metal bowl.

Variations This is a lovely treat to enjoy all year round – just choose the fruits according to availability. Strawberries, raspberries and blueberries are perfect in summer.

Following the Filling & Healthy day approach?
For this recipe use 4 of your weekly *ProPoints* allowance per serving.

ProPoints values to spare?

+1 per dessert by making the recipe with an extra 2 tablespoons of whipping cream.

+2 by serving each dessert with an extra 60 g (2 oz) scoop of low fat vanilla ice cream.

+2 by sprinkling 15 g (½ oz) of grated chocolate over each dessert.

FRESH BERRY
Sponge

A whisked sponge uses no fat, which makes it light and airy, and relatively low in *ProPoints* values – so it's worth mastering the technique.

5 *ProPoints* values per serving
ProPoints values per recipe 37

 Serves 8
Preparation time 25 minutes
 Cooking time 8–9 minutes

calorie controlled cooking spray
3 large eggs
100 g (3½ oz) caster sugar
100 g (3½ oz) plain flour
200 g (7 oz) low fat soft cheese
finely grated zest of 1 lemon
1 tablespoon icing sugar
2 tablespoons lemon curd, mixed
    with 1 tablespoon hot water
200 g (7 oz) raspberries
100 g (3½ oz) blueberries
fresh mint leaves, to decorate

1 Preheat the oven to Gas Mark 7/220°C/fan oven 200°C. Spray two 18 cm (7 inch) sandwich tins with the cooking spray and line the bases with circles of baking paper.

2 Using a hand-held electric mixer, whisk the eggs and sugar together in a large bowl until very pale and light in texture – this will take about 5 minutes on full power. To check that the mixture is thick enough, switch off the mixer and lift up the beaters – they should leave a trail in the mixture for a few seconds.

3 Sift the flour into the mixture and fold it through lightly but thoroughly, using a large metal spoon. Divide the mixture between the prepared tins and level the tops.

4 Bake the cakes for 8–9 minutes until golden brown and springy to the touch. Remove from the oven and turn them out of the tins on to a cooling rack. Cover with a clean damp tea towel and leave until completely cold. Remove the lining paper.

5 Mix together the low fat soft cheese, lemon zest and icing sugar. Spread half the mixture over the surface of one sponge, then spread the lemon curd over it (stir it well first). Top with most of the raspberries and blueberries. Sandwich the two cakes together and decorate the top with the rest of the soft cheese mixture, the remaining berries and mint leaves.

Cook's tip The secret of success is to whisk the eggs and sugar together until they increase in volume, then carefully fold through the flour so that you don't lose the air you've just whisked in.

Following the Filling & Healthy day approach?
For this recipe use 4 of your weekly *ProPoints* allowance per serving.

BANANA
Cake

It takes just 15 minutes to make this easy banana cake, and about an hour to bake it. It's that simple.

ProPoints values per serving
ProPoints values per recipe 55

 Serves 12
Preparation time 15 minutes

 Cooking time 1 hour + cooling

225 g (8 oz) self-raising flour
a pinch of salt
100 g (3½ oz) margarine
100 g (3½ oz) light muscovado or
    caster sugar
¼ teaspoon freshly grated nutmeg
2 large eggs
1 teaspoon vanilla extract
450 g (1 lb) bananas (weighed with
    skins)

1 Preheat the oven to Gas Mark 4/180°C/fan oven 160°C. Line a 900 g (2 lb) loaf tin with baking paper.

2 Put the flour into a large mixing bowl and add the salt. Rub in the margarine with your fingertips until the mixture looks like fine breadcrumbs. Stir in the sugar and nutmeg.

3 Beat the eggs and vanilla together. Peel and mash the bananas with a fork or potato masher. Stir the eggs and bananas into the rubbed in mixture until thoroughly combined.

4 Tip into the prepared tin and bake in the centre of the oven for 55–60 minutes, until firm and golden.

5 Cool in the tin on a wire rack for 30 minutes, then turn out carefully and cool completely.

Cook's tip Cut into 12 equal pieces and freeze what you don't need, so that you're not tempted to eat too much.

Variation Use mixed spice instead of nutmeg, or leave out the spices altogether.

Following the Filling & Healthy day approach?
For this recipe use 4 of your weekly **ProPoints** allowance per serving.

ProPoints values to spare?

+1 per piece by making a topping with 300 g (10½ oz) low fat soft cheese mixed with 2 tablespoons of icing sugar and 1 teaspoon of finely grated lemon zest.

STRAWBERRY AND LEMON
Butterfly Cakes

These pretty little cakes are perfect for a teatime treat.

5 ProPoints values per serving
ProPoints values per recipe 61

Serves 12
Preparation time 15 minutes
Cooking time 20 minutes + cooling

125 g (4½ oz) margarine
125 g (4½ oz) caster sugar
2 eggs, beaten
75 g (2¾ oz) strawberries, chopped
1 teaspoon vanilla extract
1 teaspoon finely grated lemon zest
150 g (5½ oz) self-raising flour

For the topping
100 g (3½ oz) low fat soft cheese
15 g (½ oz) icing sugar
1 teaspoon lemon juice
½ teaspoon finely grated lemon zest
6 strawberries, halved, to decorate

1 Preheat the oven to Gas Mark 4/180°C/fan oven 160°C. Put 12 paper or silicone cake cases into a bun tray.

2 Beat the margarine and caster sugar together in a large mixing bowl until light and fluffy. Gradually add the eggs, beating well between each addition. Stir in the chopped strawberries, vanilla extract and lemon zest.

3 Sift in the flour and fold it in gently using a large metal spoon. Share the mixture between the cake cases.

4 Bake in the centre of the oven for 18–20 minutes, until risen and golden. Cool in the tin for a few minutes, then transfer to a wire rack to cool completely.

5 To make the topping, beat together the low fat soft cheese, icing sugar, lemon juice and lemon zest.

6 Slice the tops off the cakes and cut them in half. Spoon the topping on to the cakes, place the sliced cake halves on top and decorate with half a strawberry.

Following the Filling & Healthy day approach?
For this recipe use 5 of your weekly **ProPoints** allowance per serving.

ProPoints values to spare?

+1 by spooning 1 heaped teaspoon of strawberry jam on to each cake before adding the soft cheese topping (see above).

+1 per cake by using mascarpone cheese instead of low fat soft cheese for the topping.

SPICED CRANBERRY
and Banana Muffins

If you love baking, try a batch of these delicious muffins. Freeze some so you have them handy for a packed lunch or an afternoon treat.

6 ProPoints values per serving
ProPoints values per recipe 45

Serves 8

Preparation time 20 minutes

Cooking time 30 minutes + cooling

125 g (4½ oz) low fat spread, melted and cooled slightly

2 tablespoons skimmed milk

1 teaspoon vanilla extract

2 large eggs, beaten

100 g (3½ oz) self-raising flour

1 teaspoon ground mixed spice

50 g (1¾ oz) light muscovado sugar

50 g (1¾ oz) dried cranberries

75 g (2¾ oz) porridge oats

1 banana, mashed

1 Preheat the oven to Gas Mark 4/180°C/fan oven 160°C. Line 8 holes of a muffin tin with muffin cases or squares of baking paper.

2 Mix together the cooled low fat spread, skimmed milk, vanilla extract and eggs.

3 In a large mixing bowl, combine the flour, mixed spice, sugar, cranberries and porridge oats.

4 Stir the wet ingredients into the dry ingredients with the mashed banana, taking care that you don't over-mix. Spoon into the prepared muffin cases.

5 Bake for 25–30 minutes, until firm and golden brown. Cool the muffins on a wire rack.

Cook's tip The secret of successful muffins is to make sure that you don't over-mix the wet and dry ingredients.

Following the Filling & Healthy day approach?
For this recipe use 4 of your weekly *ProPoints* allowance per serving.

ProPoints values to spare?

+1 per muffin by making a topping with 200 g (7 oz) low fat soft cheese mixed with 4 teaspoons of icing sugar and 1 teaspoon of finely grated orange zest and sharing it between the muffins.

+1 by serving each muffin with 1 tablespoon of half fat crème fraîche.

+1 by sharing 125 g (4½ oz) mascarpone cheese between the muffins, spreading it on top. Finish off with fine shreds of orange zest, if you like.

MUESLI MORNING
Munchies

These are just the thing to round off your breakfast, or enjoy one with a mid-morning coffee or afternoon tea.

 3 *ProPoints* values per serving
ProPoints values per recipe 52

 Serves 16
Preparation time 15 minutes
 Cooking time 15 minutes + cooling

100 g (3½ oz) low fat spread
4 tablespoons golden syrup
125 g (4½ oz) porridge oats
125 g (4½ oz) low sugar muesli
50 g (1¾ oz) ready-to-eat dried
    apricots, chopped
50 g (1¾ oz) sultanas or raisins
½ teaspoon ground mixed spice
1 large egg, beaten

1 Preheat the oven to Gas Mark 4/180°C/fan oven 160°C. Put 16 paper bun cases into bun trays.

2 Melt the low fat spread in a large saucepan, then stir in the syrup and add the porridge oats, muesli, apricots, sultanas or raisins and mixed spice. Stir in the beaten egg, mixing thoroughly.

3 Spoon the mixture into the bun cases, then bake for 12–15 minutes until firm. Cool on a wire rack.

Cook's tip Store the munchies in an airtight tin for up to 5 days, or pack them in a freezer box and freeze for up to 3 months.

Variation Add dried cranberries instead of sultanas or raisins. *ProPoints* values per serving will remain the same.

Following the Filling & Healthy day approach?
For this recipe use 2 of your weekly *ProPoints* allowance per serving.

ProPoints values to spare?

+1 per munchie by adding 75 g (2¾ oz) chopped almonds or hazelnuts to the mixture.

+1 by serving each munchie with 100 ml (3½ fl oz) of unsweetened orange juice.

Filling & Healthy index

Recipe	Page	Serves	ProPoints values (used from your weekly 49)
Baked nectarines with summer berries	42	4	0
Baked potato fillers – Spicy beans and peppers	102	2	0
Carrot and ginger soup	20	6	0
Cauliflower, squash and spinach curry	38	4	0
Char-grilled asparagus salad	26	4	0
Country cottage pie	52	4	0
Fennel, rocket and red grapefruit salad	28	2	0
Griddled pepper and tomato salad	24	4	0
Grilled fish with tomatoes, lemon and chives	88	4	0
Grilled lemon salmon with leek and caper mash	126	2	0
Ham, leek and red pepper tarts	106	6	0
Hampshire watercress soup	22	4	0
Mega-veg steam fry	32	2	0
Perfectly posh jellies	44	4	0
Poached autumn fruits	46	4	0
Potato and onion hotpot with crispy bacon	142	4	0
Roast butternut wedges with chilli and cumin	34	4	0
Sea bass with fennel, orange and cannellini beans	148	4	0
Spiced roast vegetables	36	4	0
Spiced summer veg supper	168	4	0
Super-berry blitz	16	4	0
Thai vegetable bowl	40	4	0
Tuna, red onion and mixed bean lunch	182	2	0
Two-potato salad	86	2	0
Zero hero soup	18	6	0
Allotment frittata	166	6	1
Baked potato fillers – Feta with cucumber and tomato salsa	102	2	1
Carrot, cumin and red lentil dip	92	6	1
Classic fish pie	68	4	1
Creamy vegetable soup	116	6	1
Cumin-spiced cauliflower and squash	84	4	1
Griddled courgettes with feta and peas	98	4	1
Grilled haddock with prawn and Cheddar topping	178	4	1
Leek and potato soup	118	4	1
Marvellous minestrone	114	6	1
Midweek chicken roast	110	4	1
Steak and pepper goulash	130	4	1
Strawberry mousse with smashed amaretti	206	6	1
Baked potato fillers – Curried chicken	102	2	2
Cappuccino crèmes	192	4	2
Chicken, leek and barley broth	90	4	2
Couscous and quinoa salad	104	4	2
Crispbread toppers – Cottage cheese and Marmite	100	2	2
Crispbread toppers – Curried chicken and mango	100	2	2
Crispbread toppers – Tuna and cucumber	100	2	2
Ham and asparagus rolls	86	2	2
Muesli morning munchies	218	16	2
Roast loin of pork with a rosemary and thyme crust (whole joint)	64	4	2
Weight Watchers all-day breakfast	50	4	2
Asian prawn noodle salad	94	4	3

Recipe	Page	Serves	ProPoints values (used from your weekly 49)
Weight Watchers all-day breakfast	50	4	2
Asian prawn noodle salad	94	4	3
Chicken schnitzel	138	4	3
Pork saltimbocca	132	4	3
Quick beef and pepper noodles	176	4	3
Strawberry and apple crumbles	194	4	3
Wasabi smoked salmon wraps	180	2	3
Apple and blackberry cheesecake sundaes	204	2	4
Banana cake	212	12	4
Cauliflower cheese soup	152	4	4
Chocolate sponge puddings	188	6	4
Fresh berry sponge	210	8	4
Hot lemon sauce puddings	198	4	4
Mango, kiwi and raspberry knickerbocker glories	208	4	4
Moroccan-spiced turkey steaks	174	4	4
Plum beautiful tarts	196	8	4
Sausage, egg, chips and baked beans	140	4	4
Spiced cranberry and banana muffins	216	8	4
Bacon, egg and tomato salad	162	2	5
Baked aubergine Parmigiana	120	2	5
Chilli con carne	54	4	5
Crispbread toppers – Lemon curd and banana	100	2	5
Garden pitta pizzas	146	4	5
Hot roast chicken salad	172	4	5
Houmous and carrot salad bruschetta	154	4	5
Mexican salsa melts	156	4	5
Potato and aubergine moussaka	74	4	5
Squidgy carrot cake	190	12	5
Strawberry and lemon butterfly cakes	214	12	5
Veggie spag bol	78	4	5
Asparagus, courgette and plum tomato pasta	96	4	6
Orzo pasta and ham salad	150	4	6
Ramen noodles with chilli and chicken	136	4	6
Spring lamb stew	134	4	6
Chicken fusilli	158	2	7
Chicken pasanda	60	4	7
Curried lamb pittas with coriander raita	160	2	7
Fish finger sarnie	124	2	7
Home-made turkey burger	56	4	7
Perfect prawn biriyani	70	2	7
Roasted vegetable lasagne	72	4	7
Tortilla, tomato and aubergine stack	108	4	7
Ultimate red Thai chicken curry	58	4	7
Gnocchi with roasted peppers, peas and Parmesan	170	4	8
Lamb and apricot tagine	66	4	8
Leek, pea and parsley risotto	122	4	8
Macaroni cauliflower cheese	76	4	8
Sweet chilli duck with sesame noodles	82	4	8
Chicken casserole with sage and onion dumplings	62	4	9

V denotes a vegetarian recipe